Arsenal
Angel
Farringdon
Barbican
St. Paul's
Chancery Lane
Escalator Link
Monument for Bank
London Bridge
2096

This is

PRIVATE!

KEEP OUT!

NOTES

Well! After all the fuss last year Marcus never did get a peep at my private jottings - Sven was peeping all the time though, naughty boy. And here they are in a limp edition, not my favourite state but the publishers say it's for the best. I looked up a few entries the other day... there on Tuesday 13 September I found a note about visiting my publisher and slipping something into his lap. Cheeky thing was so keen on telling me about this limp edition and what the hard one would do for my bank balance I went quite faint. Anyway here it is and all for £4.99. Even Marcus won't pass one up for that price!

Love Dorien

DORIEN'S DIARY

by

DORIEN GREEN

NOTES

Grateful thanks to Laurence Marks and Maurice Gran for putting my thoughts in order; to Lesley Joseph...oh and to my mother, where would she be without me.

This edition published in 1994

First published in Great Britain in 1993 by
PAVILION BOOKS LIMITED
26 Upper Ground, London SE1 9PD

Dorien's Diary is based on the character Dorien Green from the Alomo Productions Ltd/BBC TV series Birds of a Feather

Designed by
Bridgewater Books/Peter Bridgewater and Suzie Hooper

A CIP catalogue record for this book is available from the British Library.

ISBN 1 85793 286 2

Printed and bound in Great Britain by
Butler and Tanner Ltd, Frome and London

2 4 6 8 10 9 7 5 3 1

This book may be ordered by post direct from the publisher. Please contact the Marketing Department.
But try your bookshop first.

DORIEN'S DIARY

My Intimate Confessions

by

DORIEN GREEN

Notes

Latin ... Greek *dolikhos* long, Gothic ... from *indulgēre*, ... *indulgus* firm) —**inˈdulge**... —**inˈdulg**...**ingly** *adv.*
indulgence (ɪnˈdʌldʒəns) *n.* **1.** the act of indulging or state of being indulgent. **2.** a pleasure, habit, etc., indulged in; extravagance: *fur coats are an indulgence.* **3.** liberal or tolerant treatment. **4.** something granted as a favour or privilege. **5.** *R.C. Church.* a remission of the temporal punishment for sin after its guilt has been forgiven. **6.** *Commerce.* an extension of time granted as a favour for payment of a debt or as fulfilment of some other obligation. **7.** Also called: **Declaration of Indulgence.** a royal grant during the reigns of Charles II and James II of England giving Noncon...

INDULGENCE.

by

~~DORIEN GREEN~~

DAVINA VERTE

Pussy Golightly lay back in her sunken marble bath, the exquisite scented foam rising around her alabaster shoulders like a cape of swan down. She inhaled deeply of the heady scent "Lustvixen ", the hundred dollars a bottle fragrance that had helped make her the world's leading nouveau perfumier. And as Pablo, her silent but attentive Catalonian masseur -she often wondered how one mute from birth could possess such a fluent tongue when the language was the international tongue of sexual excess ~~(that will do nicely)~~ - soothed and smoothed the little aches from her languid limbs, she let her mind drift. Could it really be only a year since her husband Martin, the founder of "Heavenly Scent Inc" had been murdered by Amazonian tribesmen while searching the Matto Grosso for new and rare ungents? She squealed with delight as she was suddenly brought back to the present by Pablo, who had taken a deep breath, plunged his head into the foaming bath-water, and was now investigating Pussy Golightly's very own Matto Grosso, for who knew what.

"Enough of that" she snapped, hauling him up by the ears. "Much as I adore your slavish devotion, I have things to do today that will not wait while I tarry with you!"

~~And so saying, she stood up, magnificent,~~ flawless. Who would imagine it was the body of a woman of nearly 36? Immediately Pablo ran to fetch a huge Christian Dior towel ling robe of whitest Egyptian cotton and wrapped her in it. Pussy strode across the priceless Persian carpet into her opulent bedroom. There, laid out on the hand built Heals of London canopied four poster, were her clothes. She was due to do lunch with her merchant bankers, so the selection had to be discreet. Her two faithful maids Karen and Stacey, understood her needs perfectly, The long weeks of training had paid off.

Ralph Lauren?

As Pussy allowed Pablo to powder her all over with silky talc from the Sex Goddess range, she smiled to remember how hapless the two coarse but well meaning cockney sisters had been when first they had come to work for her. Vulgar but grateful, for had she not rescued them from a life of
begging on the mean streets of

Edmonton?

While Pablo ministered to her body, she completed her make up. It took seconds. She still had the skin of a teenager, and needed very little in the way of cosmetics. Why try to improve on perfection, she always said. Her toilette complete, Pussy started to dress; slowly, sensuously, enjoying the feel of the rich fibres against her skin. First an ivory satin basque from Fredericks of Hollywood, then ten denier silk stockings by Christian Lacroix, palest coffee with the hint of a sheen. It amused her to know her under garments would drive any normal merchant banker wild. If only there were not covered by the austere b ut undeniably expensive classic Chanel suit she now shrugged on. Finally, the handmade lustrous calf leather stilettoes. There She looked at herself in the mirror.

If this was not the woman who was about to persuadeLondon's most cautious bankers space to part with seventy million pounds for her to expand her business, the she (n) wanted to know who it was.

In the back of her chartreuse and cream coloured Bentley Continental, Pussy looked longingly at the neck of Kurt, her muscular Austrian chauffeur, sexually alert inside his tight black Jean Paul Gaultier uniform. She wondered if there was time to order him to pull the car over come into the back, and indulge her sudden need for a fast, furious, fantastic... But no. She glanced at the little jewelled chronometer on her wrist, thirty five £45,000? thousand pounds from Horologie du Geneve, a love token from Sultan Ibn Said of Oman -or as she always thought of it "Oh, man!" There just wasn't time.

The mahogany lined lift whispered her to

the penthouse director's suite of Abercrombie and Fortescue's City of London HQ. There a uniformed flunky-in interestingly tight breeches, she noted-ushered her into a magnificent boardroom. It was empty. Pussy sat at the gorgeous Hepplewhite oaken board table, and opened her Gucci briefcase. She removed her Mont Blanc platinum nibbed fountain pen, her Smythson's tan kangaroo hide organiser, her gold plated Sony tape recorder-she kept a verbatim record of every encounter, business and pleasure-and her tiny but powerful Okaynooki palm top computer. She needed no lawyers or accountants to help her close this deal. She was a woman, alone, proud, capable.

The door opened. Pussy looked up. Her eyes widened in surprise for standing there was not old Mr Abercrombie. Instead she was looking into the cool amused grey eyes of someone she had not seen for over ten years. Her mind rushed back to a beach in Barbados, a summer's night, the sweet smell of Bougainvilleas, and the deep American tones of one Leroy Barrington whispering in her ear "Have you ever had a threesome with a dolphin?"

She snapped her mind back to the present. Leroy-tall, handsome, muskular, hung like a bison Leroy-was speaking in his honeyed South Carolina drawl. "Well Miss Pussy, how superb to meet you again after all these years. Had you headr I'd joined Abercrombie's?" Pussy shook her head, for once lost for words.

"Okay" He continued "Let's get down to business, and I'd appreciate it if you'd stop undressing me with your eyes."

Pussy knew nothing of that meeting. It was as if the past, washing over her in huge waves of reminiscence, regret, longing and belonging had wiped clean the slate of her consciousness as the spring tide eradicates a child's sandcastle. That or else too much vintage Krug for breakfast. But no, Pussy had never been one to let even the finest wines fog her brain. No, it wasn't wine, it was Leroy Barrington who had had this effect on her. As always, Damn him and his irresistable charm, his fifty thousand dollar smile, his dark pulsating man root..

The next sensation she was fully aware of was the lustrous caress of softest leather on her cheek. She opened her eyes, and was immediately disappointed to realise that she was merely feeling the Bentley's buttery

hide upholstery on against her mouth,
and not the crotch of her chauffeurs
polished calf skin breeches. She pulled
herself into an upright position, and
fumbled in ~~hex~~ the recesses of her Chanel
clutch bag for the tiny golden tape
recorder. She pressed the rewind button
and listened ~~to~~ as the tape whirred back
to it's beginning. What had she said or
done in Abercrombie and Fortescue's historic
headquarters? Pussy listened to the play-
back. What a relief! Despite Leroy's ~~di~~
dizzying prescence, it didn't sound as if
she'd given anything away! Her voice came
across as calm, determined, even amused,
although she'd never been on auto pilot.
(Let's face it, she thought, I've been
on most kinds of pilot in my time).

She listened, almost with admiration

continues ...

to her voice telling the merchant bankers of her exciting plans to expand worldwide, hoe the demand for her sensational natural beauty range was growing every day, and the that the bank that turned dow n her request on demand, for seventy million would go down in history alongside xxx the man who turned doen the Beatles, and whoever it was told the Wright Brothers if God h ad meant us to fly he'd have given us the sort of digestive systems that could cope with in fk flight food. Her pulse raced as she listened to her forceful presentation. Surely they had agreed? She opened her briefcase. Probably a cheque for the money nestled in the suede lined recesses even now? But then his voice came swimming like honey and molasses out of the tiny speaker of the tape recorder.

"A very pers uasive and exciting proposal,

Ms Golightly, or do you mind if I call
you Pussy? And one wxx which I can see
has my partners champing at the bit in
their impatience to invest in your business
dreams. But I feel a more prolonged and
private consideration of every aspect of
your corporate plan is required before
pen can be put to pape r. Shall we say my
placc, eight p.m. tonight and perhaps you
ought to bring a toothbrush?"

As the Bentley turned into the sweep ing
carriage drive of xh her Belgravia

NOTES

mansion, Pussy coloured at the sound of Leroy's arrogant Southern tones. The man had virtually propositioned her, before the board of a seven hundred year old merchant bank. The cheek of the man! And she was still fuming and fulminating at his presumption as she threw a few flimsy silk items into an overnight bag, stopped only to add her new diaphragm and her favourite handcuffs, and then hurried into the dressing room, calling for Karen and Stacey, to choose the clothes with which she would, that night, close the deal.

The two willing cockney servants bustled in in their pigeon toed way.

"Yes Madam?"

"Something sensuous and easy to get off." Pussy commanded, with a knowing smile.

INDULGENCE!

The Players:

1. PUSSY GOLIGHTLY

Dallas type
Power dresser
No scruples
Naturally beautiful
Instinctively intelligent
Huge appetites
West coast body

(Based on me, Dorien Green

2. Karen & STACEY

Losers

(cont.....)

NOTES

(cont...)

Flat chested
Bow-legged
Un-educated
Suburban

based on
Sharon & Tracey

3. MARTIN GOLIGHTLY

~~Dead~~ based on Marcus.

4. LEROY BARRINGTON

forceful wheeler-dealer
Works hard & plays hard
Muscular, chiselled body
A rod of iron with a heart of gold

based on Luke

S. PABLO - Silk-~~tongued~~
Anxious ~~to please~~
Attentive to Pussy's every need

Based on Troy

The Plot

* Pussy Golightly, world famous beauty and multi-talented, self-made billionaire from ~~Chigwell~~, New York, revolutionizes the world perfume industry with her innate charm, sex appeal & potent new smells.
* She is completely irresistible to all men
* Boardroom & bedroom battles aplenty.

LOTS of sex, shopping, film stars, hairdos, a murder or two, leg waxes, kidnappings, holidays, sun, sea, sand, ski-ing, snow, calendars, condoms, fashion shows, paparazzi political scandals, champagne, caviar, jacuzzis, saunas, baby oil, leather, handcuffs... secret agents, fast cars, fast men & one woman who has the strength to create a world she could believe in.

a photo story by Dorien Green.

Oh God! there goes Melanie. She should NEVER be wearing THAT with her figure. Is she going to notice me....?

Hi Melanie! Just a few bits & pieces - Found

(Marcus's cards in his trousers. It was too good an opportunity to miss...

...Besides, I'm WORTH IT!!

JANUARY

M	T	W	T	F	S	S
31					1	2
3	4	5	6	7	8	9
10	11	12	13	14	15	16
17	18	19	20	21	22	23
24	25	26	27	28	29	30

FEBRUARY

M	T	W	T	F	S	S
	1	2	3	4	5	6
7	8	9	10	11	12	13
14	15	16	17	18	19	20
21	22	23	24	25	26	27
28						

MARCH

M	T	W	T	F	S	S
			1	2	3	4
5	6	7	8	9	10	11
12	13	14	15	16	17	18
19	20	21	22	23	24	25
26	27	28	29	30	31	

APRIL

M	T	W	T	F	S	S
				1	2	3
4	5	6	7	8	9	10
11	12	13	14	15	16	17
18	19	20	21	22	23	24
25	26	27	28	29	30	

MAY

M	T	W	T	F	S	S
31						1
2	3	4	5	6	7	8
9	10	11	12	13	14	15
16	17	18	19	20	21	22
23	24	25	26	27	28	29

JUNE

M	T	W	T	F	S	S
		1	2	3	4	5
6	7	8	9	10	11	12
13	14	15	16	17	18	19
20	21	22	23	24	25	26
27	28	29	30			

JULY

M	T	W	T	F	S	S
				1	2	3
4	5	6	7	8	9	10
11	12	13	14	15	16	17
18	19	20	21	22	23	24
25	26	27	28	29	30	31

AUGUST

M	T	W	T	F	S	S
1	2	3	4	5	6	7
8	9	10	11	12	13	14
15	16	17	18	19	20	21
22	23	24	25	26	27	28
29	30	31				

SEPTEMBER

M	T	W	T	F	S	S
			1	2	3	4
5	6	7	8	9	10	11
12	13	14	15	16	17	18
19	20	21	22	23	24	25
26	27	28	29	30		

OCTOBER

M	T	W	T	F	S	S
31					1	2
3	4	5	6	7	8	9
10	11	12	13	14	15	16
17	18	19	20	21	22	23
24	25	26	27	28	29	30

NOVEMBER

M	T	W	T	F	S	S
	1	2	3	4	5	6
7	8	9	10	11	12	13
14	15	16	17	18	19	20
21	22	23	24	25	26	27
28	29	30				

DECEMBER

M	T	W	T	F	S	S
			1	2	3	4
5	6	7	8	9	10	11
12	13	14	15	16	17	18
19	20	21	22	23	24	25
26	27	28	29	30	31	

CALENDAR 1993

JANUARY

M	T	W	T	F	S	S
				1	2	3
4	5	6	7	8	9	10
11	12	13	14	15	16	17
18	19	20	21	22	23	24
25	26	27	28	29	30	31

FEBRUARY

M	T	W	T	F	S	S
1	2	3	4	5	6	7
8	9	10	11	12	13	14
15	16	17	18	19	20	21
22	23	24	25	26	27	28

MARCH

M	T	W	T	F	S	S
1	2	3	4	5	6	7
8	9	10	11	12	13	14
15	16	17	18	19	20	21
22	23	24	25	26	27	28
29	30	31				

APRIL

M	T	W	T	F	S	S
			1	2	3	4
5	6	7	8	9	10	11
12	13	14	15	16	17	18
19	20	21	22	23	24	25
26	27	28	29	30		

MAY

M	T	W	T	F	S	S
31					1	2
3	4	5	6	7	8	9
10	11	12	13	14	15	16
17	18	19	20	21	22	23
24	25	26	27	28	29	30

JUNE

M	T	W	T	F	S	S
	1	2	3	4	5	6
7	8	9	10	11	12	13
14	15	16	17	18	19	20
21	22	23	24	25	26	27
28	29	30				

JULY

M	T	W	T	F	S	S
			1	2	3	4
5	6	7	8	9	10	11
12	13	14	15	16	17	18
19	20	21	22	23	24	25
26	27	28	29	30	31	

AUGUST

M	T	W	T	F	S	S
30	31					1
2	3	4	5	6	7	8
9	10	11	12	13	14	15
16	17	18	19	20	21	22
23	24	25	26	27	28	29

SEPTEMBER

M	T	W	T	F	S	S
		1	2	3	4	5
6	7	8	9	10	11	12
13	14	15	16	17	18	19
20	21	22	23	24	25	26
27	28	29	30			

OCTOBER

M	T	W	T	F	S	S
				1	2	3
4	5	6	7	8	9	10
11	12	13	14	15	16	17
18	19	20	21	22	23	24
25	26	27	28	29	30	31

NOVEMBER

M	T	W	T	F	S	S
1	2	3	4	5	6	7
8	9	10	11	12	13	14
15	16	17	18	19	20	21
22	23	24	25	26	27	28
29	30					

DECEMBER

M	T	W	T	F	S	S
		1	2	3	4	5
6	7	8	9	10	11	12
13	14	15	16	17	18	19
20	21	22	23	24	25	26
27	28	29	30	31		

CALENDAR 1995

JANUARY

M	T	W	T	F	S	S
30	31					
1	2	3	4	5	6	7
8	9	10	11	12	13	14
15	16	17	18	19	20	21
22	23	24	25	26	27	28

FEBRUARY

M	T	W	T	F	S	S
		1	2	3	4	5
6	7	8	9	10	11	12
13	14	15	16	17	18	19
20	21	22	23	24	25	26
27	28					

MARCH

M	T	W	T	F	S	S
		1	2	3	4	5
6	7	8	9	10	11	12
13	14	15	16	17	18	19
20	21	22	23	24	25	26
27	28	29	30	31		

APRIL

M	T	W	T	F	S	S
					1	2
3	4	5	6	7	8	9
10	11	12	13	14	15	16
17	18	19	20	21	22	23
24	25	26	27	28	29	30

MAY

M	T	W	T	F	S	S
1	2	3	4	5	6	7
8	9	10	11	12	13	14
15	16	17	18	19	20	21
22	23	24	25	26	27	28
29	30	31				

JUNE

M	T	W	T	F	S	S
			1	2	3	4
5	6	7	8	9	10	11
12	13	14	15	16	17	18
19	20	21	22	23	24	25
26	27	28	29	30		

JULY

M	T	W	T	F	S	S
31					1	2
3	4	5	6	7	8	9
10	11	12	13	14	15	16
17	18	19	20	21	22	23
24	25	26	27	28	29	30

AUGUST

M	T	W	T	F	S	S
	1	2	3	4	5	6
7	8	9	10	11	12	13
14	15	16	17	18	19	20
21	22	23	24	25	26	27
28	29	30	31			

SEPTEMBER

M	T	W	T	F	S	S
				1	2	3
4	5	6	7	8	9	10
11	12	13	14	15	16	17
18	19	20	21	22	23	24
25	26	27	28	29	30	

OCTOBER

M	T	W	T	F	S	S
30	31					1
2	3	4	5	6	7	8
9	10	11	12	13	14	15
16	17	18	19	20	21	22
23	24	25	26	27	28	29

NOVEMBER

M	T	W	T	F	S	S
		1	2	3	4	5
6	7	8	9	10	11	12
13	14	15	16	17	18	19
20	21	22	23	24	25	26
27	28	29	30			

DECEMBER

M	T	W	T	F	S	S
				1	2	3
4	5	6	7	8	9	10
11	12	13	14	15	16	17
18	19	20	21	22	23	24
25	26	27	28	29	30	31

PERSONAL

IF FOUND PLEASE RETURN TO

NAME DORIEN GREEN

ADDRESS BRYAN CLOSE, CHIGWELL, ESSEX

TEL NO 071 531 7697

PASSPORT NO 7310417 RENEWAL DATE 6/96

NATIONAL INSURANCE NUMBER How should I know?!

must get a new one it's wearing out.

BUSINESS

NAME

ADDRESS

TEL NO

TELEX FAX

MEDICAL/ACCIDENT

DOCTOR DR JACOBSON TEL NO 071 855 1321

~~NATIONAL HEALTH NO~~ PRIVATE: B17992

BLOOD GROUP O

ESSENTIAL INFORMATION 36" 22" 36"

IN CASE OF ACCIDENT PLEASE NOTIFY

NAME MARCUS GREEN

ADDRESS as above - BUT PLEASE don't let him see this diary

TEL NO

BANK

NAME Moneylink CODE NO 61-92-37

ADDRESS 10, High Street, Chigwell

TEL NO

CURRENT ACC NO 21216 7348

~~DEPOSIT ACC NO~~ Marcus's acc no: 31274871

Marcus's PIN no: 1101

CAR

REGISTRATION NO DG69 KEY NO

DRIVING LICENCE NO 1313770 AA/RAC NO 579316

INSURANCE NO ???

ADDRESS - No idea - must ask Marcus.

TEL NO

POLICY NO RENEWAL DATE

STANDING ORDERS

DATE	PAYEE	AMOUNT
1st of month	Allowance from Marcus	£12,500
14th of month	Post House Motel - Standing reservation	£235.00
30th	- Andrew	£200.00
5th	- Gardening services	£175.00

CLOTHING

How do I begin? Favourites are:

Lagerfeld, Joseph, Browns, anything from Harrods, Armani, Balenciaga.

DIARY
© BAREFACTS DIARY 1994

FRIDAY 31

7.30pm MELANIE'S PARTY

Invited to Melanie Fishman's for New Year's Eve Party. Somehow she got MARCO PIERRE WHITE to do the catering. I wonder what she did to obtain his services? – (I'm sure it's nothing she's never done before).

New Year's Day SATURDAY 1

SAW IN 1994 I got drunk on hot punch, Marcus got punched by a hot drunk & went home early. Made my New Year's resolutions :-

1) To be faithful to Marcus.
2) Never to spend more than £1500 on a single garment.
3) To help the underprivileged & mentally handicapped – like Sharon & Tracey – in that order.

SUNDAY 2

£ £ £ £ £

Sun: Marcus complains his ulcer is rumbling. Why did I marry such a hypocondriac?? Because he was very rich & I was very poor – silly question.

NOTES

M	T	W	T	F	S	S	M	T	W	T	F	S	S	M	T	W	T	F	S	S
13	14	15	16	17	18	19	20	21	22	23	24	25	26	27	28	29	30	31		

3 MONDAY New Years Day Holiday (UK and R. of Ireland)

Marcus in bed all day. Why does he never spend all day in bed with ME??! I phone his mother and tell her M's ulcer could be serious – she says he's always been a hypocodriac, I should ignore him. I make him lunch & go next door to see S&T

4 TUESDAY Bank Holiday (Scotland)

I can't help noticing this incredible hunk mowing Hugh Winsley's lawn. He smiles (!) His t-shirt is dripping sweat. I MUST NOT BREAK MY NEW YEAR'S RESOLUTION! He gives me his card – so why shouldn't I have a winter gardener as well?

NALD
ICES
ered
INGFORD
6 5454

[5 WEDNES]DAY

Go to Harrods for the first day of the sale. It's chaos. Buy some interesting French underwear which has been reduced. If it was reduced much more there wouldn't be anything left of it!!

6 THURSDAY

No sign of S & T. Have they gone away?

FRIDAY 7

I had the most amazing dream about me and MURDO – the gardener. I was most defin'itely unfaithful to Marcus .... <u>in</u> spades .... <u>on</u> spades ... <u>in</u> wheelbarrows – ENOUGH – but it was only a dream and that doesn't count.

SATURDAY 8

New French baker in the deli

Oh my God! <u>How</u> am I going to last until the <u>end</u> of January? – let alone <u>all</u> of 1994???

Shopping List
- nail varnish
- caviar
- olives - stuffed
- bagels
- aspirin
- toilet paper

SUNDAY 9

Marcus wants me to drive him to Dr. Chomsky. I do. There's nothing wrong with him..... <u>AGAIN!</u> – He has nervous bowel syndrome – CHARMING!

Dr Chomsky's clinic
081 716 7129

Harrods
KNIGHTSBRIDGE

RECEIPT

LINGERIE	
044532	£54.99
044533	£25.99
044675	£78.55
044676	£99.75
SUB TOTAL	£259.28
VAT @ 17.5%	
TOTAL	£259.28

THANK YOU FOR YOUR CUSTOM

M	T	W	T	F	S	S	M	T	W	T	F	S	S	M	T	W
10	11	12	13	14	15	16	17	18	19	20	21	22	23	24	25	26

10 MONDAY

I telephone Murdo.
It turns out he does for Melanie.
Will he 'do' for me?
-He'll look at my garden on Sunday.

11 TUESDAY

Bump into Melanie in the deli.
She says Murdo's the best gardener she's had. (When she says "had", does she mean "had" or "had"??)

12 WEDNESDAY

Saw Sharon coming home from work this afternoon....
MY GOD SHE'S FAT!
How can a woman let herself get into a state like that? No wonder she can't get a man.

13 THURSDAY

* This is going to be my lucky year!! *
Marcus has to go to Budapest on Saturday - back in a week.

JANUARY 1994

M	T	W	T	F	S	S	M	T	W	T	F	S	S
31					1	2	3	4	5	6	7	8	9

M.

FRIDAY 14

If I buy lots of indoor plants perhaps Murdo can have a look at those for me. Its about time something grew in my bedroom. OH! BUY 150 SOILED HOUSEPLANTS – that should keep him busy.

* MARCUS TO BUDAPEST *

SATURDAY 15

Marcus is up at 6. When I say 'up', I mean...... Oh never mind!.... He kisses me goodbye and says he'll phone. With any luck I'll be unobtainable

MURDO TO LOOK AT THE GARDEN ~~10-30~~ 11·00

SUNDAY 16

I dress the way any suburban housewife would dress for a 15 stone gardener from Dundee who looks like Arnold Shwarzer- or whatever his name is. Murdo arrives at 11. I tell him I have some very sick houseplants. He says he only works outside. In January?? I'm not dressed for outside.

NOTES

* DON'T FORGET THE PLANTS BEFORE SUNDAY

M	T	W	T	F	S	S	M	T	W
10	11	12	13	14	15	16	17	18	19

17 MONDAY — Murdo!!

I Break one of my New Year's resolutions.

18 TUESDAY

What a dish Murdo is! We've got quite a lot in common really – I'm into rubber – he's into rubber plants – he does work inside when pushed.... & boy did I push – I've never done it in a gazebo in January.

19 WEDNESDAY

Murdo tells me Melanie is FRIGID. I love him even more!! He asks me if I've ever been to the KYLE OF LOCHALSH (?) – I can't wait!

20 THURSDAY

Pop in to S & T's this evening. Dying to tell them about Murdo but don't.

FRIDAY 21

Sharon wants me to go with her to Harrods. Why not? Though I'm not for people like Sharon getting too familiar with places like Harrods. Its not Homebase. I see this AMAZING fioricci dress for only £2750 (it was £5500) I break the second of my New Year's resolutions - Sharon buys a Harrods mug.

SATURDAY 22

MARCUS HOME FROM BUDAPEST

Marcus phones - he's stuck in Budapest and won't be home until Tuesday - Pehaps I'll phone Murdo and take him to the Highlands tomorrow (?) He wears a kilt when he's in Scotland - Never had a man in a kilt.

MURDO 11·00 am

SUNDAY 23

Tracey comes round this morning. I try to get rid of her before Murdo arrives. I give him a copy of 'My Secret Garden' by Nancy Friday - he thinks it's a gardening book. BOY, IS HE IN FOR A SHOCK WHEN HE READS IT!!

NOTES

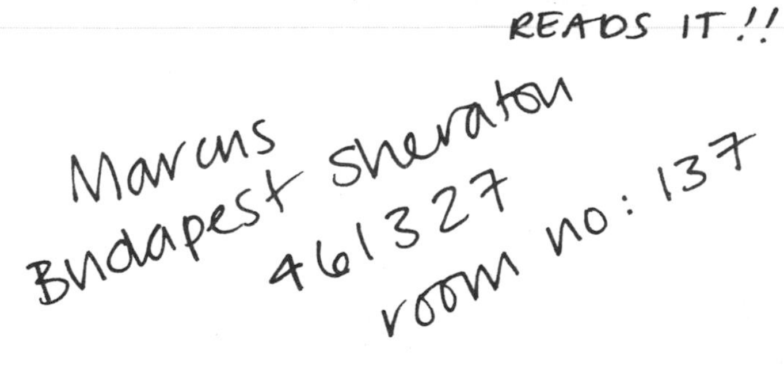

M	T	W	T	F	S	S	M	T	W	T	F	S	S	M	T	W	T	F	S	S
10	11	12	13	14	15	16	17	18	19	20	21	22	23	24	25	26	27	28	29	30

MURDO!

24 MONDAY

Murdo and I try to work out why my geraniums are not growing as they should be - Murdo says he doesn't have a problem with his ..... This man is NOT kidding.

25 TUESDAY

Marcus due home today

- I don't know what time.

26 WEDNESDAY Australia Day

Marcus arrived around midday and brought me a figurine from Hungary. I asked what he did in Budapest, he said I wouldn't understand. He asked what I did whilst he was away - I told him he wouldn't understand!!!

27 … AY

M. asks why the house is full of house plants - Don't I know he suffers from Hay Fever?

M	T	W	T	F	S	S	M	T	W	T	F	S	S
31					1	2	3	4	5	6	7	8	9

FRIDAY 28

M. offers to take me out to dinner in London, then starts sneezing violently & doesn't stop. I can't sleep with him when he's like this. Mind you – it's the nearest he ever comes to moving for more than 5 minutes.

SATURDAY 29

I telephone Murdo & suggest we go to Scotland on Wednesday and return for Sunday evening. My treat. He says he'd love me to see the Trossachs...

071/397 6173

SUNDAY 30

Tomorrow afternoon I have an appointment with my Harley St. doctor – Mr Salamone. Look into the possibilities of having my boobs enlarged.

NOTES

car hire?

booked flight BA 672 9.30 am to Inverness on 2.2.93

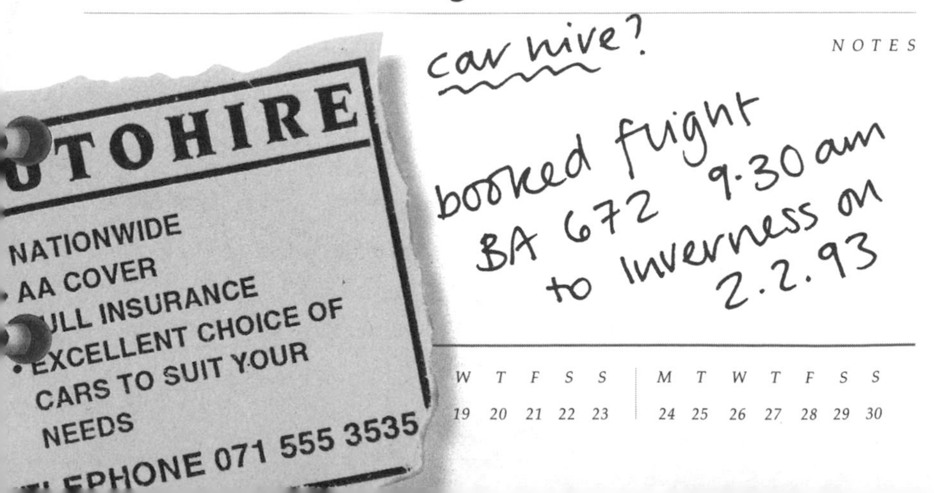

W	T	F	S	S	M	T	W	T	F	S	S
19	20	21	22	23	24	25	26	27	28	29	30

31 MONDAY Mr. Salamone says I'm too short to have a 40" bust & there's a fair chance I'd topple over. STUPID MAN! With a 40" bust I won't be on my feet that often. He asks what my husband thinks – I tell the good doctor he probably won't even notice. We lead separate lives. Then why do I want my boobs enlarged he asks? Because I want to be the

1 TUESDAY UK President of the Dolly Parton fan club. HONESTLY – how does a man like this become a cosmetic surgeon?

Tell Marcus I have to go into a 'women's only' clinic for exploratory tests tomorrow. He asks what time supper will be. I tell him I might be in overnight or two. He says he'll

2 WEDNESDAY go to his mother's for supper.

FLY 9.30 A.M.

I meet Murdo at Stansted & we fly to Inverness, then rent a car and drive to Loch Ness. We sit at the edge of the Loch and one thing leads to another..... Don't let anyone tell me there's no such thing as a Loch Ness Monster – I've seen it. I reached out & touched it!!!

3 THURSDAY

Murdo telephones Marcus and says he's a consultant and that everything is all right. "Dorien will be home on Sunday." Marcus asks if it will be lunch or dinner time? My husband is OBSESSED with food. His whole life revolves around meal times.

FRIDAY 4

MURDO WEARS HIS KILT! How he doesn't catch a cold I don't know. I often wondered what scotsman wear under their kilts – the same thing I wear under my Armani skirt – ZILCH! It just makes getting there so easy.

SATURDAY 5

We take the lift to the top of Ben Nevis. At nearly 4500ft this is the HIGHEST position I've EVER MADE IT!! – we miss the last lift down.

SUNDAY 6

RETURN FROM SCOTLAND

OH MY GOD! M. is expecting me home & we are stuck up Ben Nevis.

Murdo calms me down with those amazing biceps, pecs, & thighs of his. By midday we are down in Fort William & fly back to Stansted.

NOTES

M T W T F S S | M ... S S

14 15 16 17 18 19 20 | 21

Brain Rot Gaz 081 327 1999

FEBRUARY 1994

7 MONDAY I'm growing a little bored with Murdo. He never wants to go indoors. Gazebo's, Lochs, up mountains, the Skye to Kyle of Lochalsh ferry.... yes! BUT NEVER IN BED. Call me old fashioned, but there's something reassuring about going to sleep afterwards – NOT suffering from frostbite!

8 TUESDAY

Sharon & I go to a new wine bar in Abridge.
We get picked up by two 20 year olds – Baz and Gaz. Sharon disappears with Baz leaving me with 'Brain Rot of Britain'.

9 WEDNESDAY

* Hairdressers 9.30 *
- Facial with Marie at 12.30.

10 THURSDAY

Marcus wants to go with me to Harley Street tomorrow. He found my appointment card whilst looking for his migraine tablets. He's worried and jealous. Worried something might be wrong with me, and jealous there's not something really wrong with him.

FEBRUARY 1994

M	T	W	T	F	S	S	M	T	W	T	F	S	S
	1	2	3	4	5	6	7	8	9	10	11	12	13

FRIDAY 11

DOCTOR SALAMONE 2.15pm

Persuade M. I'd rather go alone to Harley Street. Dr. Salamone tells me that a boob enlargement job is a long process & could be dangerous. It is also very expensive and only one in ten actually take.
—They've also been known to explode in aeroplanes.

SATURDAY 12

– Tracey's for morning coffee.
I try and explain about my intended op – she keeps on about what is it? I eventually tell her but SWEAR her to secrecy. She says she wouldn't let anyone mess with her "threepennies".
Sometimes she speaks another language to normal Chigwell folk!

SUNDAY 13

Mummy's 3.00

Visit Mummy this afternoon.
GOD, Colindale is SO depressing! How did I ever live there for eighteen years???

NOTES

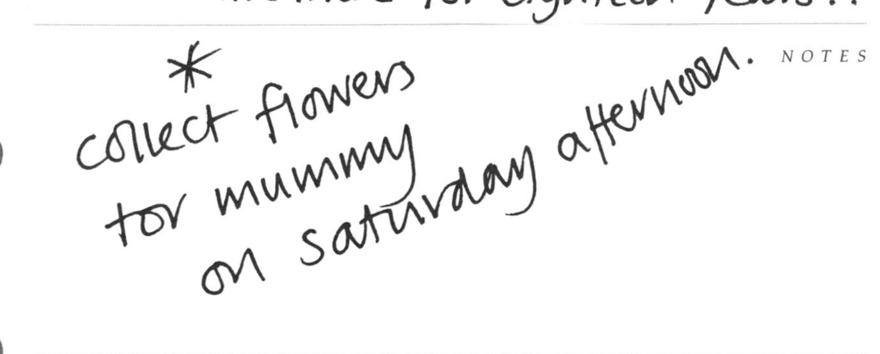

M	T	W	T	F	S	S	M	T	W	T	F	S	S	M	T	W	T	F	S	S
14	15	16	17	18	19	20	21	22	23	24	25	26	27	28						

14 MONDAY ♥ St Valentine

♥ VALENTINE'S DAY ♥ – Get up before the post-man arrives

♥

* Book manicure & pedicure for tomorrow afternoon.

(only 12 cards this year)

15 TUESDAY

- Marie 3.30 manicure etc.

Spend the afternoon getting ready for M's Lodge do tomorrow – I don't know what to wear. Think about the Balenciaga and the Conran but they're both SO boring. Sharon comes in and asks if I'd thought about 'Next'? – Where is this girl's head at?

16 WEDNESDAY M!S LODGE DO Ash Wednesday

Take a taxi to London and buy, on impulse, a lovely little Lagerfeld dress. Try and bait price down from £3500 but, because I'm paying with Marcus's Amex card, the salesman says he can't do anything on the price. Still – it's only money.

17 THURSDAY Well, that's the LAST time I'm going to one of M's Lodge affairs. The STUPID man on my right threw up down my Lagerfeld! What a common Lot. – Pulled a very nice chiropodist – Denholm. Told him I'd been suffering from hard skin. He said if I wanted to see HARD skin

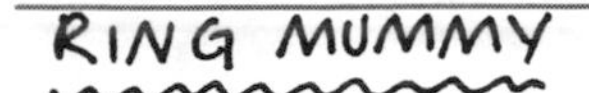

FRIDAY 18

Go to Mummy's for supper - She has a new man. She says he's a professional man, but won't tell me which profession. Marcus can't come. Business in Southampton - I sometimes think he's got a lover....

SATURDAY 19

Murdo phones completely out of the blue! Asks me if I want to go rock climbing with him. Is this a euphemism???

SUNDAY 20

6pm.... The Police call. Marcus has been in a road accident - the Jaguar is a write off. Thank God. It was only an 'F' reg. M. is in Southampton General suffering from slight concussion. The police offer to take me down to see him. I suppose I'd better go.

NOTES

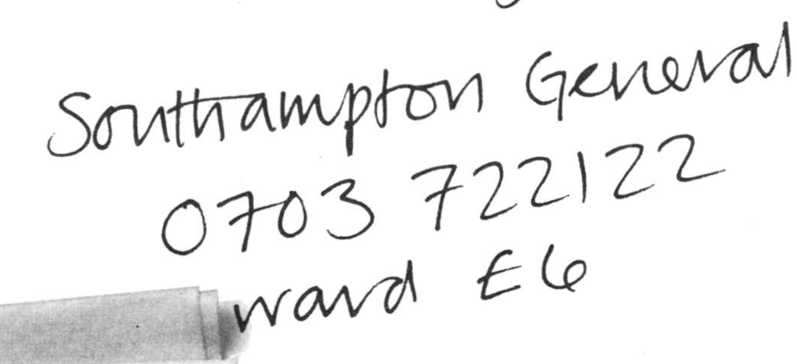

081322
1114
10am

S	M	T	W	T	F	S	S	M	T	W	T	F	S	S
20	21	22	23	24	25	26	27	28						

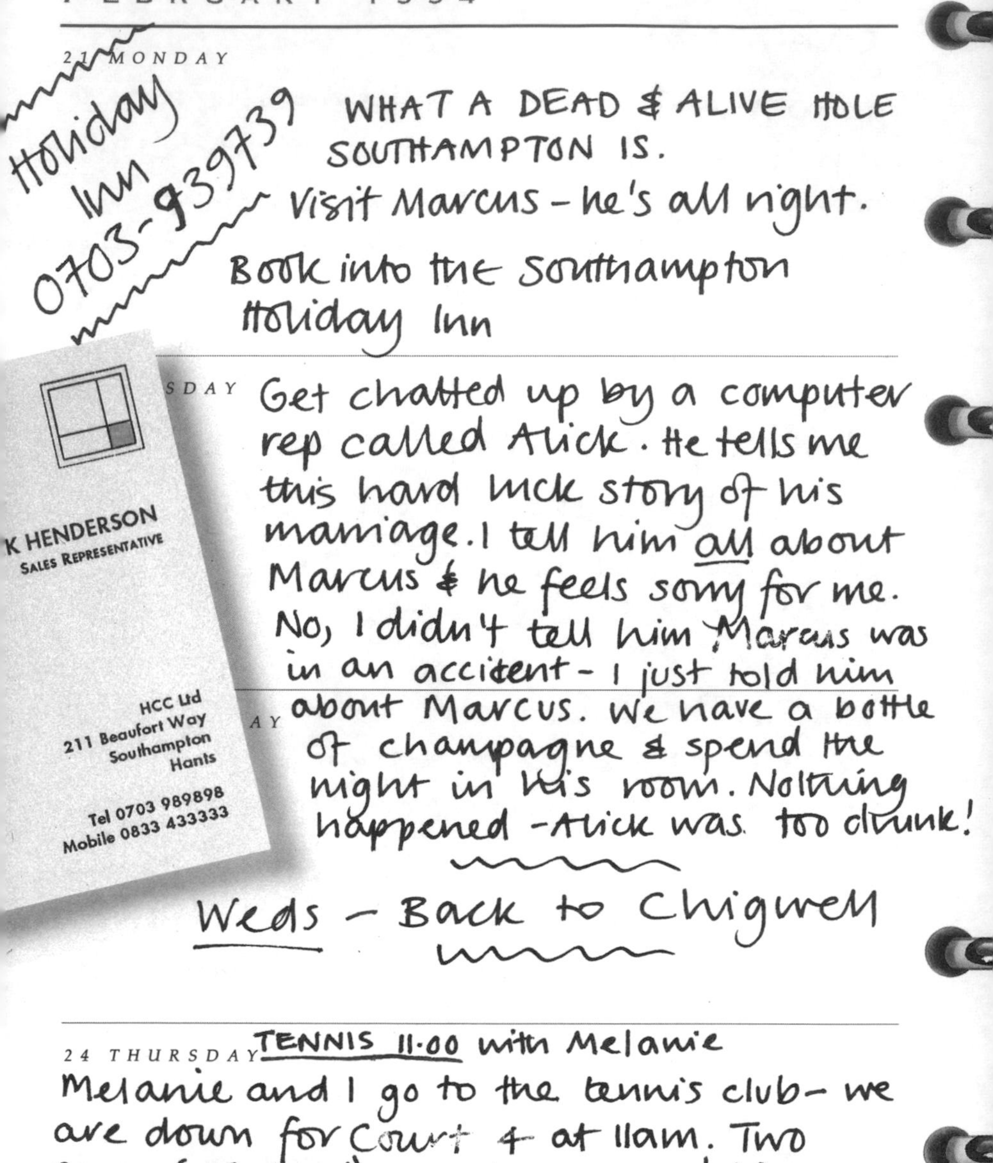

21 MONDAY

Holiday Inn 0703-939739

WHAT A DEAD & ALIVE HOLE SOUTHAMPTON IS.

Visit Marcus – he's all right.

Book into the Southampton Holiday Inn

SDAY

Get chatted up by a computer rep called Alick. He tells me this hard luck story of his marriage. I tell him all about Marcus & he feels sorry for me. No, I didn't tell him Marcus was in an accident – I just told him about Marcus. We have a bottle of champagne & spend the night in his room. Nothing happened – Alick was too drunk!

AY

Weds – Back to Chigwell

24 THURSDAY TENNIS 11·00 with Melanie

Melanie and I go to the tennis club – we are down for Court 4 at 11am. Two guys (not bad) ask if we would like a mixed doubles – I play with Simon – he's quite good. Married. Asks if I would like to have lunch with him tomorrow. Melanie's FURIOUS as her partner, Clive, is a GLOMP!

FEBRUARY 1994	M	T	W	T	F	S	S	M	T	W	T	F	S	S
		1	2	3	4	5	6	7	8	9	10	11	12	13

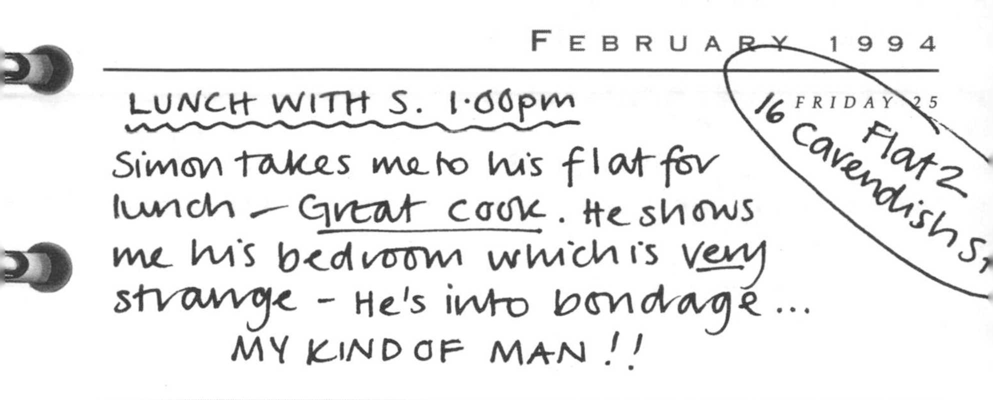

FRIDAY 25

16 Flat 2 Cavendish S…

LUNCH WITH S. 1·00pm

Simon takes me to his flat for lunch – Great cook. He shows me his bedroom which is very strange – He's into bondage … MY KIND OF MAN!!

SATURDAY 26

Went round to Simon's. Problem is I put the cuffs on him & mislaid the key. Still – his cleaning lady will be in at nine tomorrow – Perhaps she will know where he keeps a spare.

Buy some new tennis knickers

M	T	W	T	F	S	S	M	T	W	T	F	S	S	M	T	W	T	F	S
14	15	16	17	18	19	20	21	22	23	24	25	26	27	28					

S.

28 MONDAY M. GOES AWAY

Marcus off for yet another of his business trips. I suppose the air miles will come in useful one day....
Went next door but found Tracey has become addicted to Garth's computer games AND has lost the art of conversation - not that she was ever that good at it.

1 TUESDAY

Went shopping with Melanie Fishman - God knows why - she's got longer legs and better tits (though I'd never admit it to her). Nothing worth buying in all of Bond St. Suggest we pop over to Paris .....

2 WEDNESDAY

Woke up in an Emperor Louis Napoleon-size bed in Hotel Grillon - makes the Savoy look like the Basildon Post House. IF ONLY... I hadn't woken up alone. Croissants with Melanie then BLITZ Rue St. Honore - spent 25000 francs - must be losing my touch!!

3 THURSDAY

Woke up in bed alone..... AGAIN!! Briefly wondered whether the 7,000 francs I spent on lingerie had been wasted. The the waiter came in. I hadn't ordered a baguette so I know he was pleased to see me!!!

MARCH 1994

M	T	W	T	F	S	S	M	T	W	T	F	S	S
	1	2	3	4	5	6	7	8	9	10	11	12	13

FRIDAY 4

Jules, the obliging waiter, did NOT turn up with my breakfast. Felt guilty at the thought he might have got the sack for spending ALL day in bed with me. Met Melanie for brunch, learned he spent ALL night in bed with h COW!!

SATURDAY 5

* MUMMY'S BIRTHDAY *

Sent her a card and a BIG Interflora bunch of white lillies. They remind her of death. Went to synagogue because of sudden attack of Jewish guilt..... Well.... about EVERYTHING really.

SUNDAY 6

WE'RE IN GSTAAD!! - winter playground of hyper-rich Euro Trash, two of whom, Marcel & Jerome picked us up at MAXIM'S yesterday. Check into PALACE HOTEL - and forced to spend 3000 S.F. on emergency ski-wear

NOTES

Interflora
681 2121

M	T	W	T	F	S	S	M	T	W	T	F	S	S	M	T	W	T	F
14	15	16	17	18	19	20	21	22	23	24	25	26	27	28	29	30	31	

M. AWAY

7 MONDAY

Marcel wakes me at 6am! I say "NO, Marcel, not again. Five times in one night is my limit in a new country." Turns out the idiot expects me to go ski-ing just because I bought the gear! The only part of ski-ing I like is feeling the bar of the ski-lift between my thighs!

8 TUESDAY

Return to London with... LEG IN PLASTER. Should never have let Marcel persuade me onto his two-man bob - and once on it I should certainly have NEVER let him do THAT! - At least its only my ankle.

9 WEDNESDAY

Installed on sofa with fruit, chocs, books, zapper, and a terrible itch inside my plaster cast.

Sharon offers to scratch it for me with an unfurled wire hanger - As if I would allow a wire hanger in my house!!

10 THURSDAY

Still itching!

Hazelnut Surprise

Strawberry Delight

W	T	F	S		M	T	W	T	F	S	S
2	3	4	5	6	7	8	9	10	11	12	13

M.

Marcel x5

Sebastian's caterers 071 421 9752

FRIDAY 11

M. returns

Marcus returns from Dubai, very tense – successful business trip. But, he had to pretend to be a Christian.
For some reason, this has made him TREMENDOUSLY RANDY......

SATURDAY 12

MUMMY TO DINNER

Mummy due for dinner
Marcus STILL staring at my toes with that glassy David Mellor expression.
My normal caterers are busy. Sharon offers to help me out – forced to accept.

Mother's Day

SUNDAY 13

Must admit – Sharon's cooking isn't bad if your idea of a Jewish meal is saveloy, mash and beans. Rather like the look of Robin, Mummy's new man – AND, as luck would have it – he's an orthopaedic surgeon!

NOTES

Countrywide Caterers:– 8.00 on Saturday
071 497 1727
menu??

M	T	W	T	F	S	S	M	T	W	T	F	S	S	M	T	W	T	F	S	S
14	15	16	17	18	19	20	21	22	23	24	25	26	27	28	29	30	31			

14 MONDAY 12·00 lunch at Melanies.

Marcus and I invited to Melanie's for lunch. Find I can't sit comfortably in the Jaguar – persuade Marcus to hire a Bentley Turbo.
Melanie's face on our arrival made the fracture worthwhile!

15 TUESDAY

RONALD JENSEN CHARGED

YESTERDAY afternoon in Leeds, the well known entrepreneur, Ronald Jensen (46) was detai[illegible] officers

16 WEDNESDAY Marcus at Leeds Crown Court in the Ronald Jensen case.
DETERMINED NOT TO BE HOUSEBOUND – I get an agency to send a chauffeur. George arrives. Former policeman. Impeccable manners. 15 years chauffering experience. If only I fancied him. Send him away!

17 THURSDAY St. Patrick's Day

HUGHIE looks FANTASTIC in a chauffer's uniform. I bet when the deli sent him round with my smoked salmon, he never thought he'd end up in a uniform, in a Bentley, in Epping Forest, in the back seat WITH ME?!

MARCH 1994	M	T	W	T	F	S	S	M	T	W	T	F	S	S
	1	2	3	4	5	6		7	8	9	10	11	12	13

Samaritans 081 221 2211

FRIDAY 18

Marcus came home and SACKED Hughie – JUST because he didn't have a driver's licence. What a small minded attitude towards the problem of youth unemployment.

I BURST INTO TEARS!

SATURDAY 19

SUNDAY 20

Hobble to Marcus's wardrobe and cut the arms off his Georgio Armani dinner jacket.

Tracey pops in to ask if I want any shopping – I threaten her with pinking shears!

NOTES

Chauffeur
* George Barker *
arriving at
10.00am
Weds

LIMOUSINE HIRE
WEDDINGS
•
AIRPORT
•
THEATRE
MONTERARY ROAD, CHISWICK.
TEL: 081 676 2047

PERSONAL CHAUFFEUR SERVICES
...VIL WAY, WC2...071 434 2222

W T F S S | M T W T F S S
21 22 23 24 25 26 27 | 28 29 30 31

21 MONDAY

DEPRESSION OVER!! ☺

It was just PMT. Considering what a full month I've had – physically – I ought to CELEBRATE!

22 TUESDAY

→ BENS BAR MITZVAH 2·30 — present ???

Marcus & I getting ready to go to Miriam & Tony's son's Bar Mitzvah. Marcus wants to know what happened to his D.J. – I plead ignorance – He goes next door to borrow Darryl's – VERY 1988!

23 WEDNESDAY

Sitting with the papers while Marcus is playing golf. Ring on the door, I LIMP to open it and... IT'S ROBIN – mummy's friend! He just wondered how my leg felt. I invite him to feel it & tell me! – Wonder what FREUD would say??

24 THURSDAY *MARCUS IN COURT*

Marcus back to Leeds to give evidence. Robin comes round, AGAIN – what wonderful hands!! Of course, if he was my doctor it would be unethical as well as adulterous – BUT – WHO'S COUNTING??

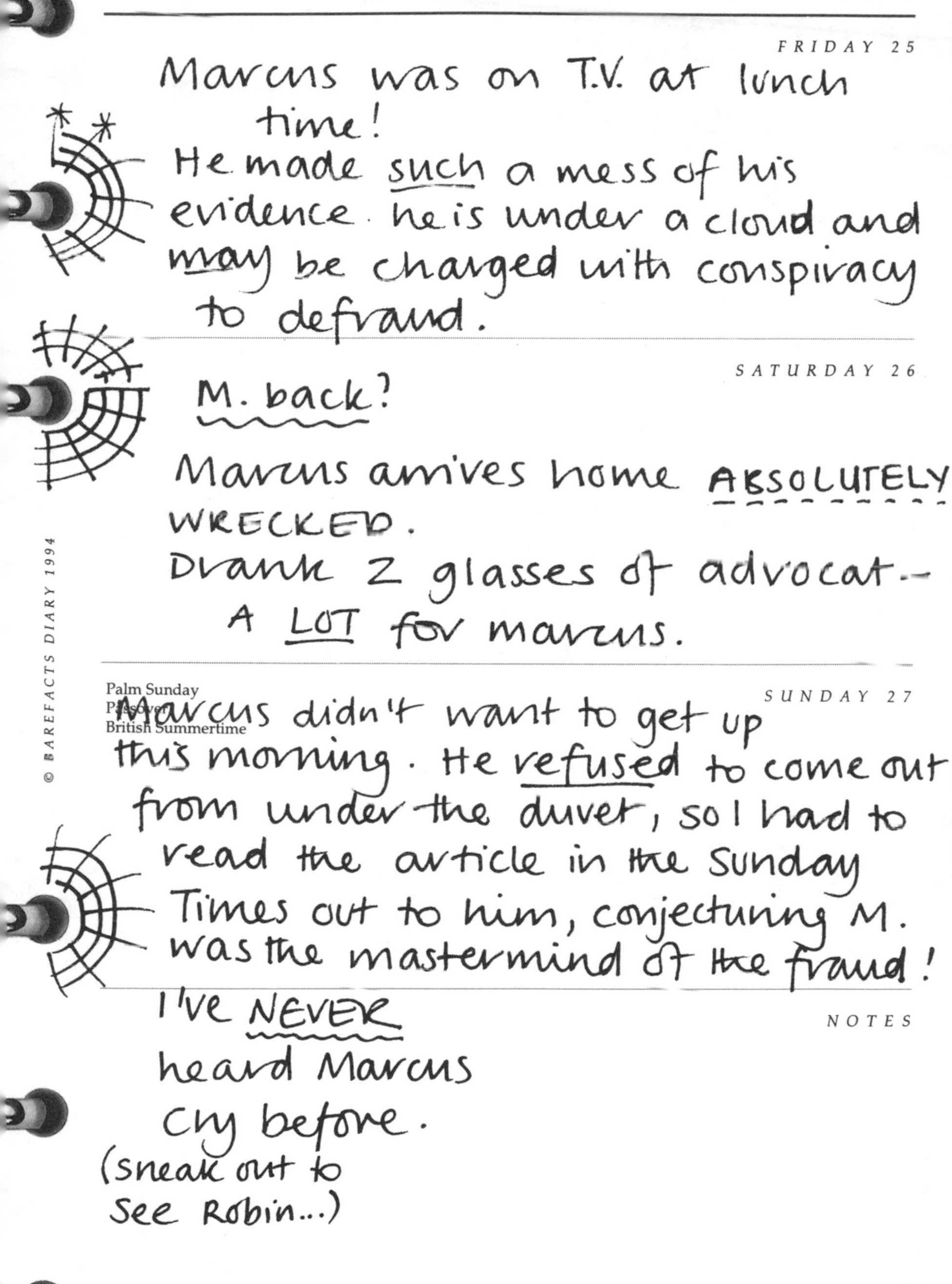

MARCH 1994

FRIDAY 25

Marcus was on T.V. at lunch time!
He made such a mess of his evidence. he is under a cloud and may be charged with conspiracy to defraud.

SATURDAY 26

M. back?

Marcus arrives home ABSOLUTELY WRECKED.
Drank 2 glasses of advocat – A LOT for Marcus.

SUNDAY 27

Palm Sunday
Passover
British Summertime

Marcus didn't want to get up this morning. He refused to come out from under the duvet, so I had to read the article in the Sunday Times out to him, conjecturing M. was the mastermind of the fraud!

NOTES

I've NEVER heard Marcus cry before.
(sneak out to see Robin...)

M	T	W	T	F	S	S	M	T	W	T	F	S	S	M	T	W	T	F	S	S
14	15	16	17	18	19	20	21	22	23	24	25	26	27	28	29	30	31			

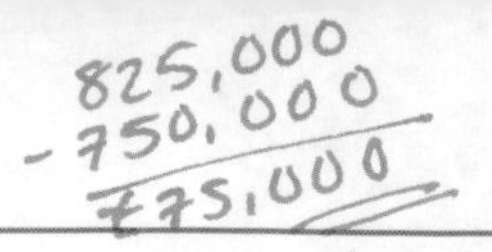

28 MONDAY PLASTER OFF – HOORAY!

Judge said M. would be in contempt if he didn't return to court, so... I'm alone again. Hughie phones and invites me to an illegal rave party instead. Danced ALL NIGHT!

29 TUESDAY

RONALD JENSEN HAS SKIPPED BAIL & fled to Indonesia!
M. was one of his sureties to the tune of £½ a MILLION!! WE COULD BE RUINED!
And I loved that Bentley. M. is helping Leeds C.I.D. with their enquiries....

30 WEDNESDAY THE HOUSE IS FOR SALE – £750,000 o.n.o. Visit M. in Leeds – he has aged 20 years. Told me I must find Ronald Jensen & bring him back to England – feel EXCITED & DRAMATIC! Sharon thought I was the punchline of a joke: "My wife went to the East Indies." "Jakarta?" "No, she went of her own accord!" – STUPID WOMAN!!

31 THURSDAY

Interesting few hours with the young Estate Agent – He agreed to raise the price to £825,000. No chance of getting a buyer at that price. – Went to Harley St. for a pre-flight check-up. Expected armfull of injections – Got a Bottom Full instead. Hope the plane has well padded seats...

Good Friday HEATHROW 8·45 FRIDAY 1

Half way to Bali I realised it was April Fools Day! Is this all a terrible wind up of Marcus' It MUST Be (?) last sunday was the first night of passover – I should have been at Marcus's mother – and I was with a randy orthopaedic surgeon instead!! What a FOOL I am to fall for M's trick.

SATURDAY 2

LAND IN INDONESIA.

No idea what day it is – How many hours ahead or behind.

MUST GET BACK TO ENGLAND!!

Easter Day SUNDAY 3

NO FLIGHTS – monsoon rain – apparently quite unseasonal. Check into the Bali EMPEROR HOTEL – 5 stars & 24 HOUR MASSAGE LINE. Maybe I'll stay a day or two...

NOTES

British Airways
Bali 62670

M	T	W	T	F	S	S	M	T	W	T	F	S	S	M	T	W	T	F	S	S
11	12	13	14	15	16	17	18	19	20	21	22	23	24	25	26	27	28	29	30	

4 MONDAY Easter Monday (Holiday in UK and R. of Ireland except Scotland)

Easter Monday – not a Bank Holiday in Indonesia (or Scotland – oddly – according to my diary).
Decide to visit a Detective agency in case Ronald Jensen is here.
GOD – IT'S HOT!

5 TUESDAY

My detective is a charming young man called Pak Lok Cuk – or something like that. He says he'll find Jensen – if he's in the country, but warns me he isn't cheap. I tell him neither am I. – I think we understand each other!

6 WEDNESDAY

100 %
URE SILK
e in Bali

I have a new wardrobe made out of silk – so cheap and ALL ready in a day. Return to Hotel.. Pak Lok Cuk, he says I can call him Cuk if I like... says he has news – but is VERY mysterious ???

7 THURSDAY

Wake up in bed with my Indonesian detective (?) No recollection at all of how he got there – either I've developed Alzheimer's overnight OR the local Champagne is to be avoided. But as he has a lithe, brown, smooth body & enormous stamina – WHO CARES??

APRIL 1994	M	T	W	T	F	S	S	M	T	W	T	F	S	S
					1	2	3	4	5	6	7	8	9	10

INDONESIA

Jensen – 4th white house – Tuk san Rd

FRIDAY 8

Realize I haven't phoned Marcus! DO SO. HE IS DISTRAUGHT! Thinks I've abandoned him – As if I'd leave the man to whom I made my marriage vows – and who signs my visa account. Hang up and spend rest of day in bed with. YOU KNOW WHO!!

SATURDAY 9

One of CUK's gumshoes (technical term for junior detectives) has found Jensen living rough in the jungle... Suppose I'll HAVE to go and see him.

SUNDAY 10

LIVING ROUGH!!!?! Ronald Jensen has a 9 bedroom, air-conditioned villa WITH pool AND airstrip! I asked if he was coming home to clear Marcus's name. He just laughed and pinched my bottom. PIG! (nice body though...)

NOTES

The Emperor Hotel
Bali

Notes

~~Pack Lock~~ Cock
2:00

M T W T ... W T F S S
11 12 13 14 15 ... 22 23 24 | 25 26 27 28 29 30

INDONESIA

11 MONDAY

PERSUADED Ronald to give me a letter exonerating Marcus.
- It took some getting out of him but.... I did what I HAD to do.... quite enjoyed it actually!

12 TUESDAY

Phoned M's solicitor and told him about letter.
He says 'not to worry, Marcus has had a nervous breakdown & been declared unfit to stand trial - What a relief!

13 WEDNESDAY

SHOULD go home but the weather is WONDERFUL! - Apparently Marcus is heavily sedated - so... what's the point??

14 THURSDAY

FOOD RIOTS IN JAKARTA...

Think I'll check out the next flight home.

APRIL 1994

M	T	W	T	F	S	S	M	T	W	T	F	S	S
				1	2	3	4	5	6	7	8	9	10

FRIDAY 15

Stop over in Dubai Duty Free – Feel VERY nervous in Arab country, but manage to buy tiny video camera – could have FUN with it back in Blighty.

SATURDAY 16

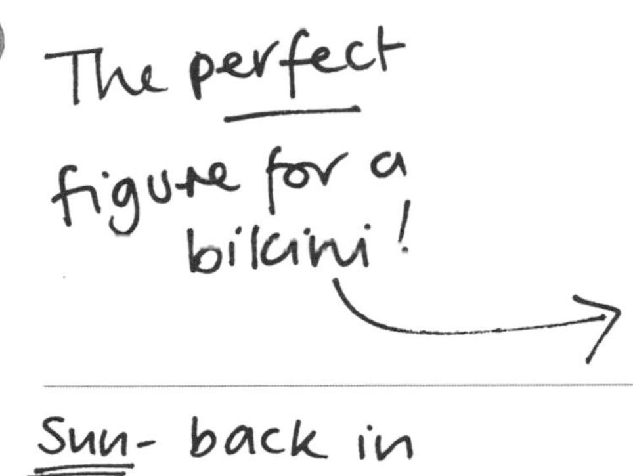

The perfect figure for a bikini!

Sun – back in London. POURING with rain. Taxi home. Big banner across the front door...

"WELCOME HOME YOU OLD SLAPPER!" – Guess who's responsible.

M	T	W	T	F	S	S	M	T	W	T	F	S	S	M	T	W	T	F	S	S
11	12	13	14	15	16	17	18	19	20	21	22	23	24	25	26	27	28	29	30	

R.J.!! BACK HOME.

 Buy the F.T.

18 MONDAY

Visit Marcus in BUPA mental retreat (as they tactfully call it). He was very quiet – seemed quite normal. Only at end of visit when he confided he was really Bet Lynch on leave from 'Coronation Street' did I start to notice something amiss.

19 TUESDAY

That nice young estate agent called round. AMAZINGLY someone has offered £850,000 for the house. A dilemma. Should we sell?? – What if Marcus never works again?!

20 WEDNESDAY

Asked next door's advice. Tracey said she'd be sorry to see me go – Sharon said, would I leave my collection of SEX TOYS behind!? – I think she'd be secretly upset too, though.

21 THURSDAY RING IRONING SERVICE.

DECIDE TO SELL – buy a flat in Regent's Park, and the change should yield an income of £3000.00 per month. I COULD live on that, just, if I'm frugal. TELL MARCUS TOMORROW.

M	T	W	T	F	S	S	M	T	W	T	F	S	S
				1	2	3	4	5	6	7	8	9	10

VISIT MARCUS AT BUPA 10.00

FRIDAY 22

Marcus is no longer Bet Lynch – He's now PC Fancy Smith of 'Z cars'. I blame UK Gold. Told him I'm going to see solicitors about obtaining power of attorney. He just said: "Roger Z Victor One"..... (??)

St George

SATURDAY 23

VIEWING 11.30

THE BUYERS, Mr & Mrs Dubrovsky, come round to view the house. Not sure what he does – looks VERY prosperous. Nice, sensitive hands, too. She looks a REAL COW! – too tanned, too much hair, overdressed, ridiculous fingernails.

SUNDAY 24

Tracey asked me about the Dubrovskys. "Was she a relation, we looked like sisters!" CHEEK!! Sharon was SURE she'd seen him on the telly.

Maybe he's a Russian film star?

NOTES

850,000
- 375,000
475,000

per month?
interest?

@ 8.92% = approx £3000 p.m.??

M	T	W	T	F	S	S	M	T	W	T	F	S	S	M	T	W	T	F	S	S
11	12	13	14	15	16	17	18	19	20	21	22	23	24	25	26	27	28	29	30	

25 MONDAY

HOUSE SALE OFF - Dubrovsky not a Russian film star - he's a Russian black marketeer with a false passport who has just been extradited to Moscow.

26 TUESDAY

* MANICURE & PEDICURE 2.30 PM

Marcus MUCH better today. Thinks he's Doctor Finlay - which is at least a step up the social ladder.

27 WEDNESDAY

M's solicitor phoned - The Ronald Jensen case is falling apart through lack of evidence. The judge is expected to throw it out today. Will I tell Marcus the good news?

28 THURSDAY

BUPA: 10.30

Visit Marcus. Try to explain about the court case. His reputation is now restored. Marcus says he never had any doubt. - After all, EVERYONE knows Rumpole of the Bailey is an honest man.

623 1667

FRIDAY 29

WOKE UP VERY DEPRESSED. Realized I hadn't had a man for weeks! – Get my address book out to start phoning round when in walks Marcus – He's discharged himself.

SATURDAY 30

Start day in dreadful suspense – who will M. think he is today??! Wonder about hiding the 'Radio Times'. Confide my fears to S&T who laugh at me. Obviously Marcus had only been pretending to be mad to avoid the trial –

SUNDAY 1

I rush home & confront him. He says he can't believe my naivety. Of course he was pretending.
(maybe there's more to M. than meets the eye?)

now that is sexy!

SUNDAY – one thing hasn't changed re Marcus – He's still as sexy as a plate of tripe.
MUST GET LAID – thoroughly & soon!!

M	T	W	T	F	S	S	M	T	W	T
11	12	13	14	15	16	17	18	19	20	2

MAY 1994

2 MONDAY Bank Holiday

Decide to go shopping to see what I can pick up. Wander round local supermarket with arms full of Clingfilm. GORGEOUS young branch manager called Jason asks if he can be of assistance I arrange to meet him on Wednesday

3 TUESDAY BRUCE OLDFIELD SHOW 2.30PM ?

Melanie comes over to ask if I want to go to the Bruce Oldfield fashion show - She sees all the clingfilm. Strange, she doesn't ask what it's for - Perhaps she knows.... Tracey comes in and asks. I say 'What do you normally use clingfilm for?' Tracey says "wrapping cucumbers." EXACTLY!

4 WEDNESDAY

MEET JASON - He asks about the bulk buying of clingfilm - what is it with clingfilm?? We take his car, an Opel Kadett, to see Top Gun 2. He's seen it 3 times, but he likes it. I suggest we go for a drive. Park the car on Hampstead Heath. It's PITCH BLACK! I tell him I can now show him what the clingfilm was for - but I haven't got any clingfilm with me - we use Bacofoil. It's not the same - DON'T try it!

5 THURSDAY

Wake up feeling DREADFUL. I bet I caught something on Hampstead Heath last night.... this morning! I mean, who in their right mind would lay down on wet grass, NAKED, at the begining of May? And believe me - BACOFOIL ISN'T WATERPROOF!

MAY 1994	M	T	W	T	F	S	S	M	T	W	T	F	S	S
	30	31					1	2	3	4	5	6	7	8

JASON & THE CLINGFILM!

FRIDAY 6

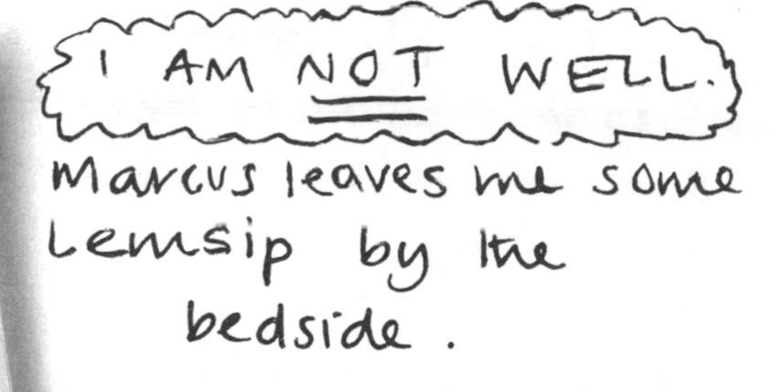

List
- more Lemsip
- Aspirin
- Tissues
- Ginseng
- Throat sweets

SATURDAY 7

Feel lousy. Feel even worse when a new Crime Prevention officer calls to talk about security. He says he can give me as much time as I like. Why do men who look like this – (Gerard Depardieu) only seem to call when I'm ill? I ask if he could come back on Thursday?

SUNDAY 8

SUNDAY: Tracey comes in and 'does' for me. She sits and talks, as freely as she can, about her sex life with Darryl. She's never been with another man! How can she compare??

NOTES

Jason

Tel: 623 6399

M	T	W	T	F	S	S	M	T	W	T	F	S	S	M	T	W	T	F	S	S
9	10	11	12	13	14	15	16	17	18	19	20	21	22	23	24	25	26	27	28	29

9 MONDAY Ascension Day

Feel a little better this morning. Suggest to M. – 'perhaps I ought to go somewhere warm for a few days?' He says 'Bournemouth'. I say Antigua. He says he can't get the time off. Why should that bother me?

10 TUESDAY

The cold has gone. The sore throat has started. Still – it sounds sexy on the phone! Another hunk calls – to read the gas meter. Just my luck! 2 men in 4 days I would happily have performed the MOST indecent acts upon, and I'm laid up…

11 WEDNESDAY

BOOK SESSION AT HEALTH CLUB

…not laid! What makes my illness worse is Marcus keeps phoning to see how I am!

Feel MUCH better this morning – particularly as I booked the flight to Antigua.

12 THURSDAY

Ask Tracey if she would come with me to buy swimwear – although I shall go TOPLESS – naturally. The Crime Prevention Officer returns – His name is Douglas and I ask him if he thinks my bedroom is secure? We discuss this over gin & tonics.

MAY 1994	M	T	W	T	F	S	S	M	T	W	T	F	S	S
	30	31					1	2	3	4	5	6	7	8

FRIDAY 13

S, T & I take taxi to Knightsbridge – (only £52). I see a gorgeous thong in grey leather. MUST have it. Sharon says she wouldn't mind trying one on. THIS I HAVE TO SEE! Tracey puts her off it – Thank God. Buy one for each day Also some, (8) outfits, for the evening, though the thongs should be more than enough

SATURDAY 14

ANTIGUA – 12.30 HEATHROW

Fly to Antigua – M. sees me off. Tears fill his eyes (petrol fumes). Sit next to a black god called KENELM – It's an old English name which means BRAVE HELMET – I SHOULD BE SO LUCKY!!

SUNDAY 15

Weather S.E.N.S.A.T.I.O.N.A.L.

Boy who brings my breakfast – SENSATIONAL. Says he's never done it before with a white lady. Keeps calling me 'Ma'am'. Who DOES he think I am? The Queen? Dine with KENELM...

NOTES

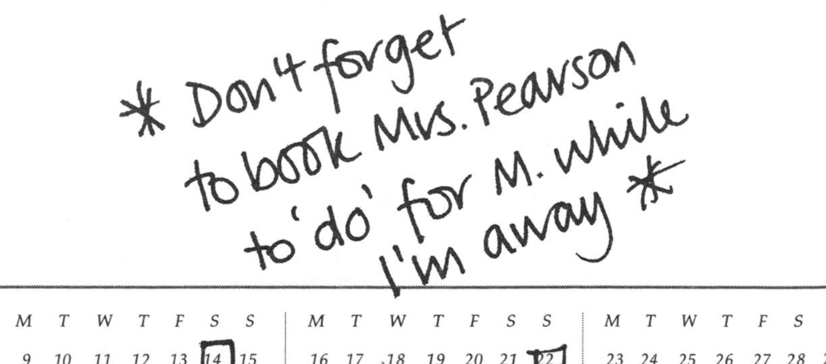

M	T	W	T	F	S	S	M	T	W	T	F	S	S	M	T	W	T	F	S	S
9	10	11	12	13	14	15	16	17	18	19	20	21	22	23	24	25	26	27	28	29

ANTIGUA (14) RETURN (22)

16 MONDAY

'BRAVE HELMET' – What a night! This man used to be a professional athlete and together we did a MARATHON! – Only it wasn't my feet which were sore this morning.... M. phones to see how I am. I tell him I think I'm going down with something.... again. He feels sorry he isn't with me. I THANK my lucky stars.

17 TUESDAY

sunbathe ALL day in the navy thong. An American business man called Edward says I have the 'greatest' ass in Antigua. By 'greatest' – he means 'best'. Sharon has the greatest in terms of VOLUME....

18 WEDNESDAY

Edward is 'into' oil – works for MOBIL. As I too am into oil (rubbed lightly ALL over my body) we hit it off in a BIG – and I do mean BIG – way!

19 THURSDAY

Edward is a group consultant and he calls another member of this group, DEAN, to play a little game that involves THREE people, a yam and oil – THIS IS THE LIFE!!!

M	T	W	T	F	S	S	M	T	W	T	F	S	S
30	31					1	2	3	4	5	6	7	8

CONFIRM FLIGHT.

FRIDAY 20

Wake up to find Edward and Dean AND JERKY (!) all in my bed. Those rum punches made me forget what the 4 of us did. But Jerry captured it all on video. BOY!! how is it possible to....? MUST try to see something of ANTIGUA today.

SATURDAY 21

MUST catch some sun. Marcus is bound to ask why I am the same colour as I was in London. - Spend the day in the sun with Kenelm — ME on top. I want the sun on my back. OH! KENELM! I want to marry you!!

Pentecost

SUNDAY 22

RETURN TO LONDON - Fly back to London with sunburn. My back is raw. My back, my ass, as Edward called it, AND the soles of my feet. I was on "mount" Kenelm for 6 hours, and the oil he rubbed all over me wasn't Ambre Solaire, but coconut oil. Apparently it TASTES better!!

NOTES

M	T	W	T	F	S	S	M	T	W	T	F	S	S	M	T	W	T	F	S	S
9	10	11	12	13	14	15	16	17	18	19	20	21	22	23	24	25	26	27	28	29

KENELM!

23 MONDAY

Marcus is at home so I go next door to S&T. Tell them about Kenelm, Edward, Dean, Jerry and the room boy whose name I never asked. They think I am a SLUT! Well, Tracey does. Sharon asked to see the video!

24 TUESDAY

Meet Melanie in Selfridges - she asks about the video. I ask how SHE knows about it? - She bumped into Sharon in the French Deli. I say I'll only show her mine if she shows me her's. Bet she's never had 3 at the same time - well, not at the SAME time!!

25 WEDNESDAY

M. says with the new technology soon he'll be able to work from home FULL TIME. HE HAS TO BE JOKING. - My sex life would come to a standstill. I try & pacify him. Tonight we do it for the 2nd time in 1994 - I think of Kenelm....

26 THURSDAY

SOTHEBY'S AUCTION 10.00

071 495 3831 SUITE 6

Auction at Sotheby's - interested in 2 items of 17th century torture apparatus. I make some FURIOUS bidding, but lose out on both to a Kenyan named Joseph.....
- He's GOT to be worth knowing.

Buy present for Craig.

MAY 1994

~~* AUNTIE SADIE'S 7.30pm *~~

FRIDAY 27

Auntie Sadie invites M & I to dinner. She's 77 and doesn't look a day over 70 - she wants Marcus to help her boyfriend's son. He's there - he's DELICIOUS - I want to help him. His name is Rodney. I bump into him in the toilet - he's coming out as I'm going in. We BOTH finish up in the bath!!...

SATURDAY 28

Rodney phones to apologise for 'shtupping' me - He didn't mean to. COURSE HE MEANT TO! He wants to have an affair with me.

I don't know!

BAR MITZVAH - BRIGHTON

Trinity Sunday

SUNDAY 29

To Brighton for M's nephew Craig's bar mitzvah. What an evening! D.U.L.L. I've been to brighter Shiva's. However, Craig's teacher, Rabbi Sherman, is very interesting. He showed me the new shul's social club hall.... by night. How do you move in on a RABBI??

M	T	W	T	F	S	S
9	10	11	12	13	14	15

M	T	W	T	F	S	S
16	17	18	19	20	21	22

M	T	W	T	F	S	S
23	24	25	26	27	28	29

M! AGAIN!

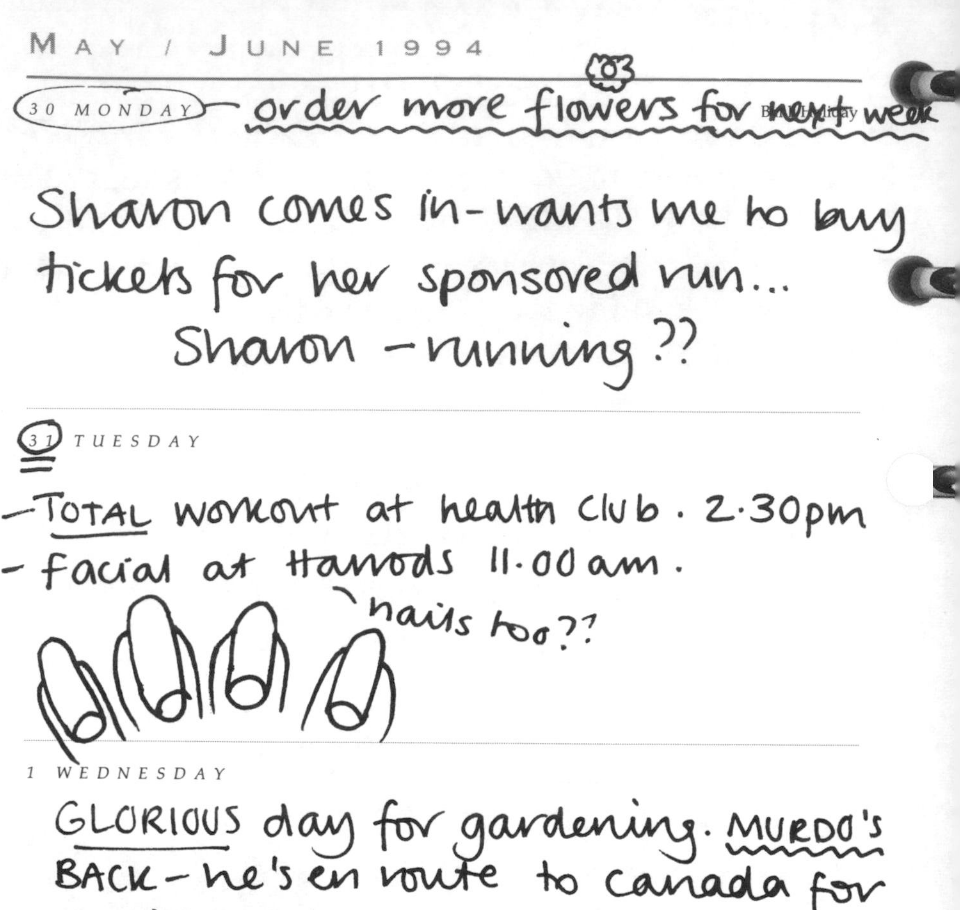

30 MONDAY — order more flowers for next week

Bank Holiday

Sharon comes in - wants me to buy tickets for her sponsored run...
Sharon - running??

31 TUESDAY

- TOTAL workout at health club. 2.30pm
- facial at Harrods 11.00 am.

nails too??

1 WEDNESDAY

GLORIOUS day for gardening. MURDO'S BACK - he's en route to Canada for a Highland Games - his plane was delayed, so he popped in "for Auld Lang Syne" to help me with my pruning...

2 THURSDAY

Nearly had a heart attack - Murdo left his sporran in the spare jacuzzi. Marcus tried to kill it with a golf club - he thought it was a RAT! Had to persuade him it was a Vivienne Westwood fashion accessory!

JUNE 1994	M	T	W	T	F	S	S	M	T	W	T	F	S	S
			1	2	3	4	5	6	7	8	9	10	11	12

FRIDAY 3

[MARCUS AWAY] Drove Marcus to Heathrow – he's off to New York to sort out the accounts of an obscure religious sect. While he was checking in... a GORGEOUS young porter in that new snazzy uniform asked if he could help with my luggage. I said I wasn't going anywhere – He said he'd see about that....

SATURDAY 4

BACK to the airport for my date with <u>DICK</u> – (I kid you not, dear diary) – He took me into the freight elevator and asked me if I wanted to join the 100 foot club??

SUNDAY 5

Invited S&T round in a moment of weakness – Sharon brought her work with her – 200lb of pickling onions to peel. Apparently her pickled onions are a <u>big</u> hit in cafe society & she peels them day & night to keep up with demand.

NOTES

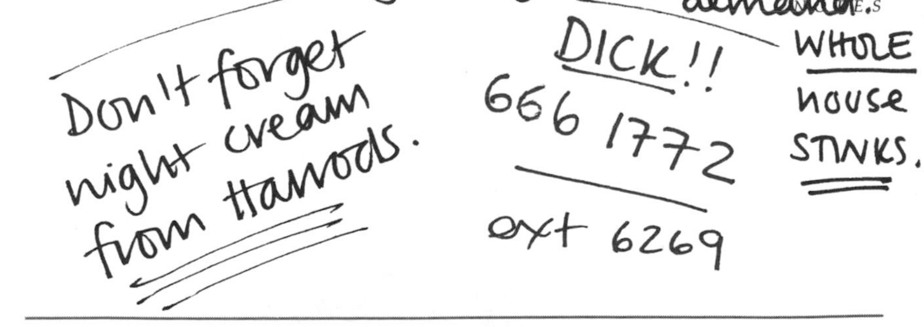

M	T	W	T	F	S	S	M	T	W	T	F	S	S	M	T	W	T	F	S	S
13	14	15	16	17	18	19	20	21	22	23	24	25	26	27	28	29	30			

Luigis Leathers
676 2047

6 MONDAY June Holiday (R. of Ireland)

BLOCKED PIPES?
SUPER-ROD
FOR COMPLETE SATISFACTION
PHONE 696969

M. Still away - HOORAY!! - Phoned SUPER-ROD about blocked sink. 25 year old HUNK came - tight jeans (no pants) - came round. Asked where's the blockage I said 'Drains OK now, but while you're here..... Had to pay overtime (Well worth it!!)

8 WEDNESDAY

WEDS - Sharon popped round to ask if I fancied trying a new wine bar, but I was too sore. Mother phoned. Her new man's dumped her.
As Pete Townsend said: "Hope I die before I get old".

9 THURSDAY

T F S S
9 10 11 12

FRIDAY 10

Mother called *again*. Wants to come and stay.
Then Marcus phoned from New York – he's lonely. Decided to send Mummy to keep him company.

SATURDAY 11

Tracey anxious when I popped over. Seems Garth's been hanging out with some bikers – Asked *my* advice. I said I'd talk to them. Went 'up West' to buy a tight leather cat suit – You never know!!

SUNDAY 12

Found the bikers café. Garthy fancies the girl behind the counter. I told her he had a starring role in EASTENDERS. She wa all over him!! – Turned my attention to Rocky & Razor, 2 mustachioed Hells Angels. I wrinkled my nose wickedly & told them I thought they could both do with a bath.
THEY SAID: Are you offering??
I SAID YES!.....

NOTES

Alf's café
146 William St
(near Joes)

13 MONDAY

ACHING ALL OVER!!

14 TUESDAY

Rocky & Razor are refusing to leave. Then, M called to say he's coming home!! Rushed next door – Sharon offered to get some heavies round, Tracey suggested a cash bribe (went with Tracey's plan).

* 15 WEDNESDAY M!S BIRTHDAY*

A.B.S.O.L.U.T.E.L.Y KNACKERED! and Marcus is demanding his conjugal rights. I said: "What do you think this is – your birthday?" HE SAID YES! Embarrassment. I pretented it was a joke, rushed to my den & gave him the present I was keeping for my lovely, sweet SVEN when he comes back from SWEDEN.

16 THURSDAY

Pretended I'd rediscovered God. Told Marcus I was going to the synagogue.
Went next door & slept for TEN hours!.

FRIDAY 17

Massage 11·30

* Buy Sven a welcome back pressie?

M.'s parents — SATURDAY 18

My in-laws visited
TOO DULL to waste ink on.

SVEN ??

Father's Day SUNDAY 19

SVEN'S BACK!! On leave from the Swedish Air Force – and I've given his suede posing pouch to Marcus, who thinks it's for keeping his golf balls dry!
Made it up to Sven in several other ways!

NOTES

DO NOT FORGET:
Birthday Present for Marcus.

M	T	W	T	F	S	S	M	T	W	T	F	S	S	M	T	W	T	F	S	S
13	14	15	16	17	18	19	20	21	22	23	24	25	26	27	28	29	30			

20 MONDAY

Woke up with 3 more grey hairs – luckily they're not on my head! Sven is at the Post House. Told Marcus I had a charity lunch. He said, "If you were having an affair, would you tell me?" I said, "OF course not." – which seemed to satisfy him.

21 TUESDAY

The boy from SUPER-ROD called back. His name's GAVIN. I didn't think to enquire before. Told me he had a new high pressure hose he wanted to demonstrate. I thought – WHY NOT??

22 WEDNESDAY

→ DOCTOR LEVY 11·30 AM

gynae? gynea

Went to my gynaecologist for regular check-up. He said everything seems OK – did his normal joke of saying if he wasn't my doctor, he'd HAVE to ravish me and STILL presented me with a HUGE bill.

23 THURSDAY

HOW CAN THIS BE??? Dr. Levy says theres NO DOUBT ABOUT IT!

FR

Actually went to the synagogue and prayed – certain I heard God laughing.

THE L
116 HARLEY ST
TEL
INVOICE NO:

*
Buy a present for tomorrow.
*

SUNDA

* FATHER'S BIRTHDAY *

Mummy came round – always gets depressed on father's birthday. As I felt suicidal too, it wasn't much fun.

NOTES

Post House Hotel
Room no:
69

M	T	W	T	F	S	S	M	T	W	T	F	S	S	M	T	W	T	F	S	S
13	14	15	16	17	18	19	20	21	22	23	24	25	26	27	28	29	30			

27 MONDAY

I've always believed in a woman's right to choose – but now I'm knocked up, I don't know if I can go through with a termination. The problem is – WHO'S THE FATHER?? make a list

28 TUESDAY

MEN I'VE HAD RECENTLY:

1. Sven
2. Gavin
3. Eric
4. Peter
5. Geoff
6. That guy from the wine Bar
7. Rocky
8. Razor – only one thing for it – seduce Marcus & persuade him its his!!

29 WEDNESDAY

Spend day planning seductive evening. fine wine, soft music, make sure M. gets a good look at my stocking tops – the he announces the Inland Revenue are auditing their books and it's rendered him IMPOTENT!

30 THURSDAY

Buy Marcus' favourite stockings

J	M	T	W	T	F	S	S	M	T	W	T	F	S	S
					1	2	3	4	5	6	7	8	9	10

wow!!

FRIDAY 1

-Phone call from Dr. Levy.
He tells me they mixed up the test results .... I'M NOT PREGNANT!
Its a Dorien Green of Chingford. I told him I didn't want to be his patient ANY Longer. He promptly asked for a date!!

SATURDAY 2

Just had INCREDIBLE SEX in the back of Dr. Levy's Range Rover -
I think I'm in love ♡

SUNDAY 3

ADMIT ONE

NOTES

meet Dr. Levy 1.30pm

M	T	W	T	F	S	S	M	T	W	T	F	S	S	M	T	W	T	F	S	S
11	12	13	14	15	16	17	18	19	20	21	22	23	24	25	26	27	28	29	30	31

4 MONDAY Independence Day, USA

Decide to celebrate by making shopping trip to NEW YORK. Booked ordinary British Airways ticket - turned up at Heathrow. Made LOUD noises about flying VIRGIN, and they bumped me up to Concorde - Always works.

5 TUESDAY

Left Bloomingdale's sales staff in a state of shock. Then on to Museum of Modern Art. Stood in front of CARL ANDRE arrangement of empty toilet rolls until an interesting young man made eye contact. His name's GREGOR - He's GORGEOUS!

6 WEDNESDAY

GREGOR IS INSANE!! I'm trapped in his loft in Alphabet City. He says - to add insult to injury - that he can't let me go because I remind him of his MOTHER!

7 THURSDAY

Escaped from Gregor by offering to have sex with him as long as he called me MUMMY.
His psyche couldn't cope and he broke down.

Mr. Jones (no 73) - Neighbourhood Watch.

JULY 1994

RETURN HOME FROM N.Y.C. 🍎 — FRIDAY 8

Back in London - Had Marcus missed me? Apparently NOT. At dinner he said: 'You've been very quiet lately, have you got a sore throat?" INSENSITIVE SWINE.

SATURDAY 9

Popped next door to see if there were any messages for me. Sharon said someone called GREGOR had left an odd message about visiting me with a MACHETE!! - She gave him my address - of course.

SUNDAY 10

Persuaded Marcus to buy a security system immediately, on account of the upsurge of crime in Greater Essex. He agreed - as long as I make all the arrangements.

NOTES

??

11 MONDAY

081-624 6242

Phoned a few security companies – Maybe they'll send round some interesting young men.....

744 6243

· alarms
· windows
· lights?

12 TUESDAY STRONG LOCK 10·00

Holiday (N. Ireland)

Strong lock consultants called – in the shape of ALISTAIR McCORMACK. A Scottish bodybuilder who would have been drummed out of the 'Chippendales' for being over-muscled. Showed him round the house. Spent rather a long time in the master bedroom...

13 WEDNESDAY *M. AWAY*

Marcus off to Penzance for 2 days – back Friday

14 THURSDAY

Alistair back with his special apparatus. He offered to wire me up for £500 – A Bargain! Half an hour later I was secured to the bed by several lengths of electrical cable .... Nice – but not what I had in mind.

JULY 1994	M	T	W	T	F	S	S	M	T	W	T	F	S	S
					1	2	3	4	5	6	7	8	9	10

FRIDAY 15

LUCKILY M. didn't return from Penzance last night as Alistair went to the car for something & locked himself out!! Spent the night in BONDAGE! (Thank God for a strong bladder). Had to use nose to phone Tracey to rescue me!!

SATURDAY 16

Have decided to renew my New Year's resolution to be faithful to Marcus – and take up something worthwhile. But what??

SUND

STRONGLOCK

THE BEST IN HOME SECURITY

ESTIMATE NO: 0176
DATE: 12·7
OUR REF: 6267

ESTIMATE

TO INSTALL SECURITY SYSTEM AND REPLACE ~~EX~~ EXISTING LOCKS AND

M

11 1

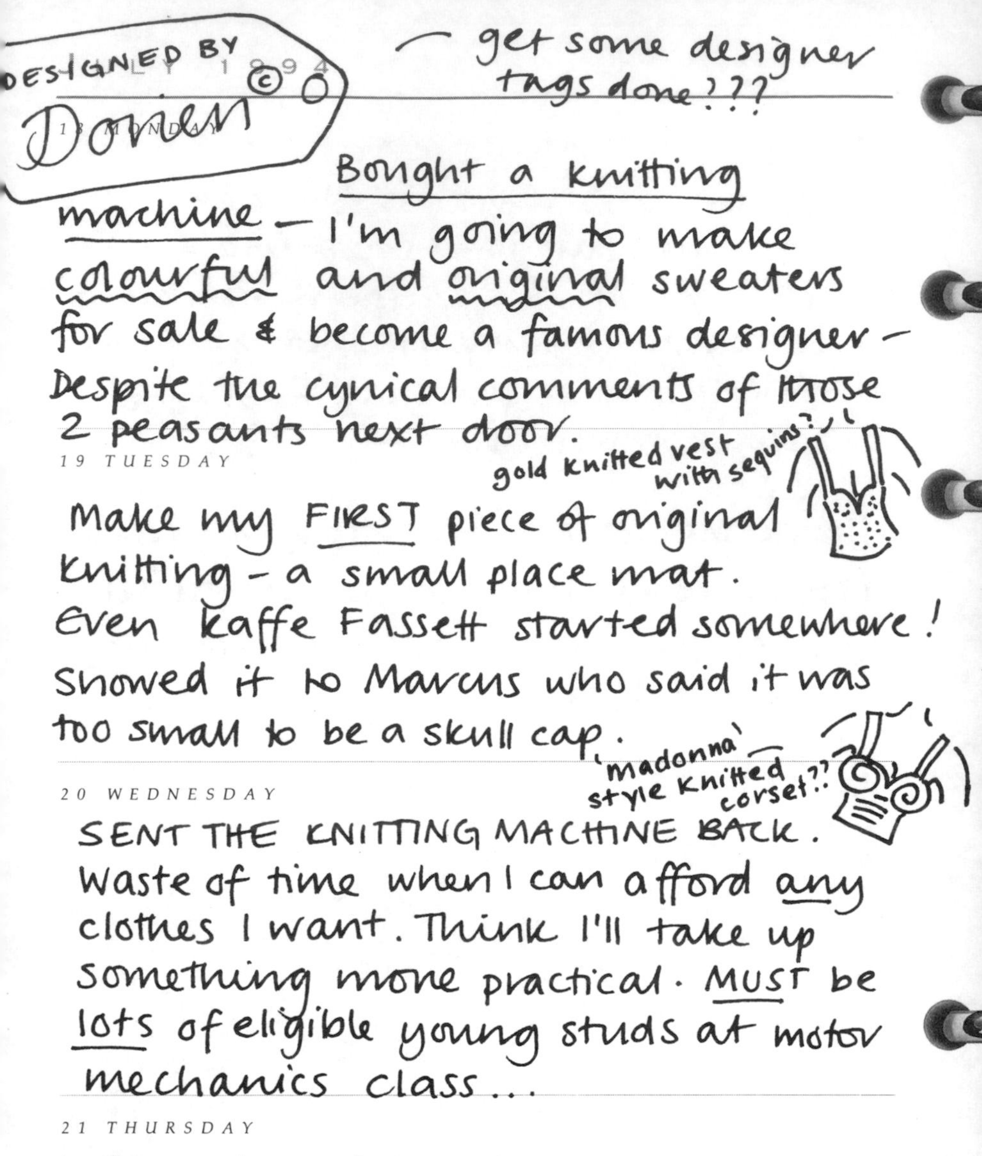

— get some designer tags done???

18 MONDAY

Bought a knitting machine — I'm going to make colourful and original sweaters for sale & become a famous designer — Despite the cynical comments of those 2 peasants next door.

19 TUESDAY

Make my FIRST piece of original knitting — a small place mat. Even Kaffe Fassett started somewhere! Showed it to Marcus who said it was too small to be a skull cap.

20 WEDNESDAY

SENT THE KNITTING MACHINE BACK. Waste of time when I can afford any clothes I want. Think I'll take up something more practical. MUST be lots of eligible young studs at motor mechanics class...

21 THURSDAY

Signed up for motor mechanics at the Evening Institute. NO MEN AT ALL! just women either looking a) for men or b) for other women.
Don't think I'm quite ready for my first Sapphic experience.

M	T	W	T	F	S	S	M	T	W	T	F	S	S
				1	2	3	4	5	6	7	8	9	10

FRIDAY 22

Alistair came back – full of apologies and aftershave. He said 'What must he do to make it up to me?' So.... I tied him to the bed – and went shopping!!

SATURDAY 23

Today I met JACQUES, a french security expert. QUELLE HUNQUE. He came round to tender for our new security system. I wanted to give it to him right away – the job – but M. insisted we see more than one expert. FAIR ENOUGH!!

SUNDAY 24

Alistair phoned with a new quotation. Shall I take him up on it??

NOTES

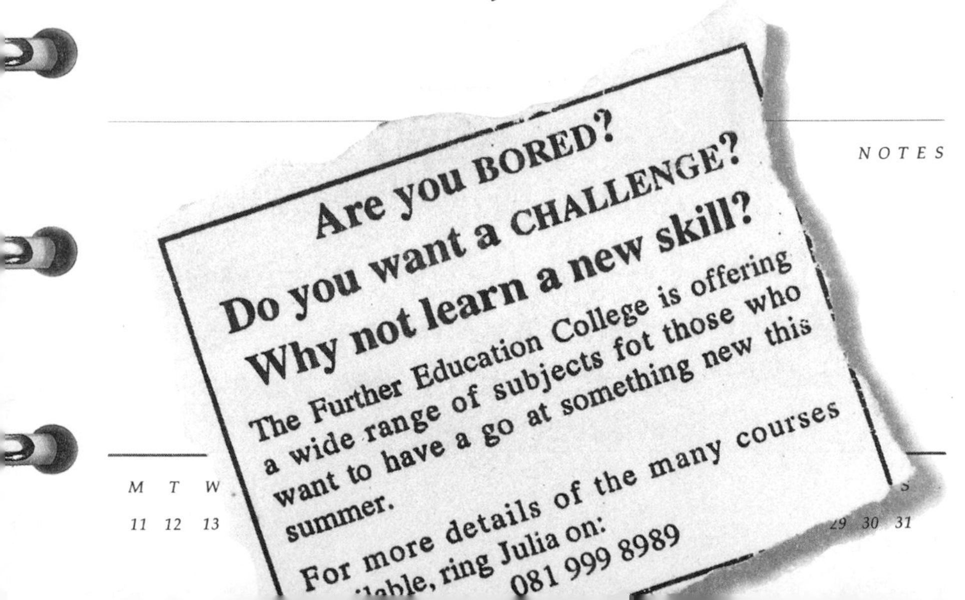

Are you BORED?
Do you want a CHALLENGE?
Why not learn a new skill?

The Further Education College is offering a wide range of subjects fot those who want to have a go at something new this summer.

For more details of the many courses
ilable, ring Julia on:
081 999 8989

M T W S
11 12 13 29 30 31

25 MONDAY

Saw Kim & Wing – two Korean students working their way through college by selling security systems – INCREDIBLE, lithe, muscular, hairless bodies – God! – I'm quivering just to think of it...

26 TUESDAY

Interviewed ROGER ex MI5 – he says – so what he doesn't know about secret places isn't worth knowing!

27 WEDNESDAY

STAYED IN BED ALL DAY, wonderfully – how can I put it – SHAGGED OUT!!

28 THURSDAY

M. asked which security company I preferred and I had to say KIM & WING – 2 Koreans in the bush are better than one in the hand.... or whatever!!

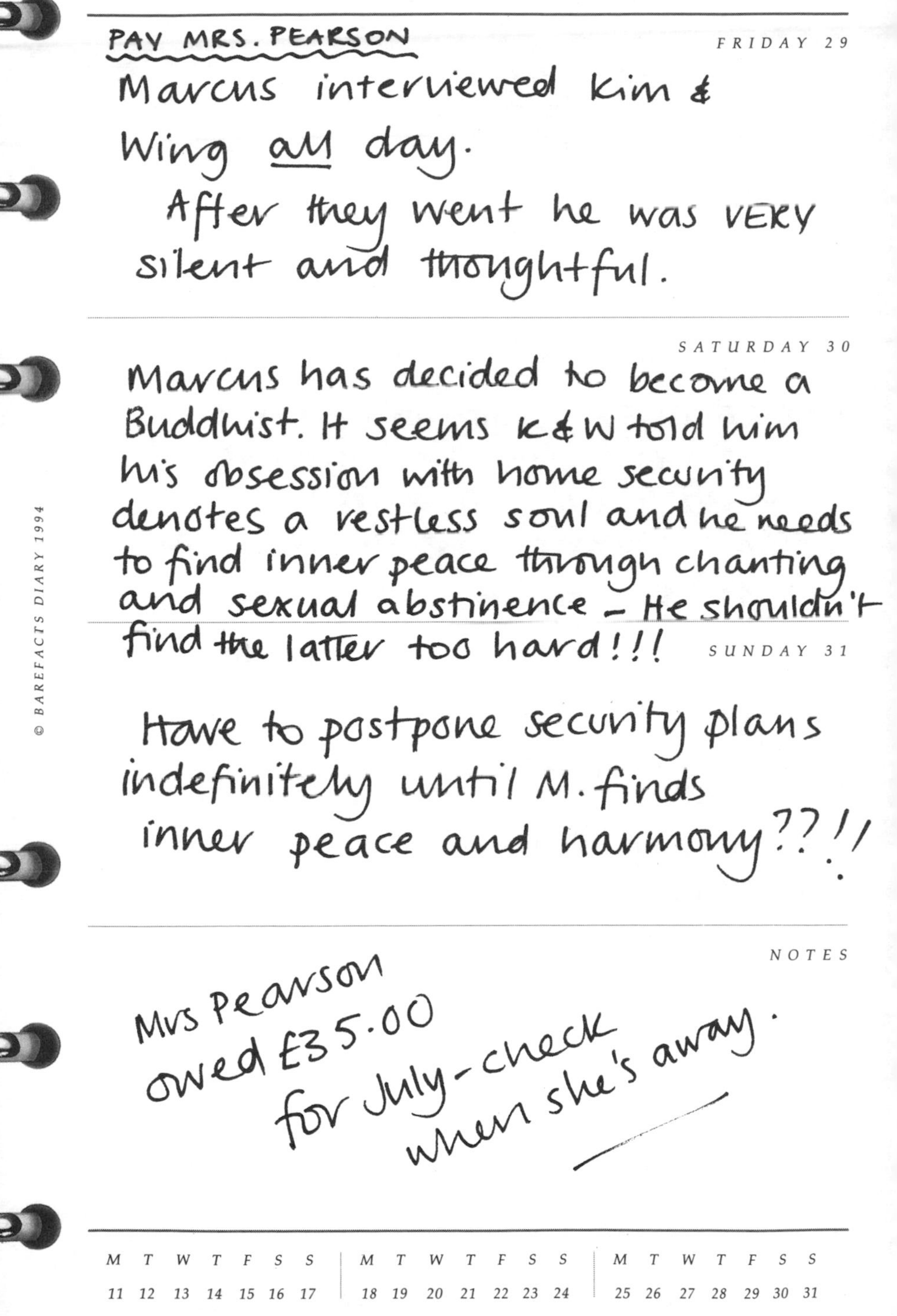
PAY MRS. PEARSON
FRIDAY 29
Marcus interviewed Kim & Wing all day.
After they went he was VERY silent and thoughtful.
SATURDAY 30
Marcus has decided to become a Buddhist. It seems K & W told him his obsession with home security denotes a restless soul and he needs to find inner peace through chanting and sexual abstinence - He shouldn't find the latter too hard!!!
SUNDAY 31
Have to postpone security plans indefinitely until M. finds inner peace and harmony??!!
NOTES
Mrs Pearson owed £35.00 for July - check when she's away.
M T W T F S S 11 12 13 14 15 16 17
M T W T F S S 18 19 20 21 22 23 24
M T W T F S S 25 26 27 28 29 30 31

Wax Factor - 117 High Street

1 MONDAY

Bank Holiday (Scotland)
Holiday (R. of Ireland)

I'M BORED!

Nothing on T.V. - no man for weeks & M. deeply into his ZEN BUDDHISM. Think I'll get the house re-modelled. Told Marcus it wouldn't cost more than £100K - He said OH!

2 TUESDAY

Phoned a succession of interior designers out of the best magazines, arranged a series of visits.
Went to WAX FACTOR (the new beauty place) for strategic hair removal in anticipation.

3 WEDNESDAY

4 Designers came round today - 3 were gay, the fourth was straight and good looking. Unfortunately, Chris was short for Christine.
Didn't invite any of them to open their portfolios.

4 THURSDAY

10·30 - LARRY

Larry came at 10.30 and changed my life. 6'3", (29) graduate of the Slade School of Fine Art, built like a bull & prepared to do the whole house for a mere £50,000. I managed NOT to say "Shall we start in the bedroom!!?"

AUGUST 1994

M	T	W	T	F	S	S	M	T	W	T	F	S	S
1	2	3	4	5	6	7	8	9	10	11	12	13	14

FRIDAY 5

Larry has some VERY UNUSUAL ideas about decor.
Very keen on the unusual positioning of furniture and light fixtures.
Hope he likes the positions I intend to suggest.....

SATURDAY 6

Not sure BLACK is the ideal colour for the living room – BUT – Larry says an artist must be given his head......
GOOD IDEA!

SUNDAY 7

UNCLE HARRY 12.30 Went out with Marcus to visit an aged uncle of his who might leave him some money When we returned Larry had started work – He had cleared all the furniture from the dining room & burned it!!
Not sure this is going to work out

NOTES

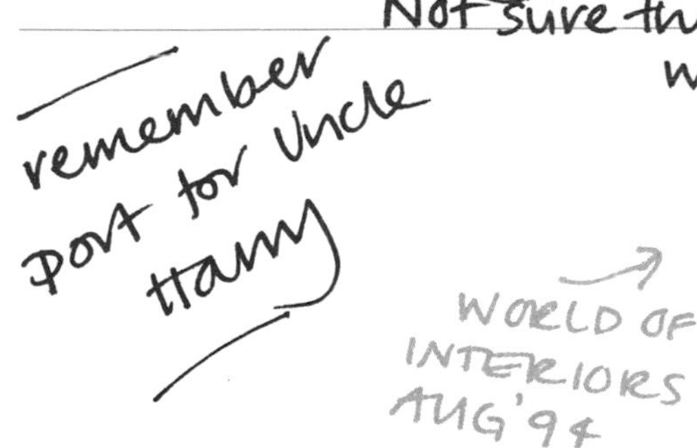

LARRY BOOTH
INTERIOR DECORATOR
Interesting Interiors for Interesting People
071 772 7777

M	T	W	T	F	S	S	M	T	W	T	F	S	S
15	16	17	18	19	20	21	22	23	24	25	26	27	28

8 MONDAY

STUDENT WRECKS HOMES

A 26-YEAR-OLD art student from West London, posing as a qualified interior designer, was helping police with their enquiries today.

Larry Bernard Booth of Wickham Place, placed advertisements in magazines ar

Item in local paper about deranged former art student talking himself into people's homes & wrecking them.

Luckily I only paid him the first £10,000

10 WEDNESDAY

Think it might be time for a holiday, as my spirits are shattered.

I know its the time of year the plebs go away – but there must be somewhere exclusive....?

11 THURSDAY

Marcus says he doesn't need a holiday because he has found inner peace & Uncle Harry has promised to leave him half a million.

(I think the old fraud is lying to get more visits). Don't want to go away alone.

FRIDAY 12

Dare I take Sharon & Tracey??

SATURDAY 13

Talk about holidays with the Cockneys. There is a difference of opinion. I favour a cultural safari through North Africa – they want to go to Disneyworld!

SUNDAY 14

Spent all day with S & T and a pile of holiday brochures. Had to persuade Sharon NOT to go topless – the world isn't ready. As usual, they're short of money – if it's going to be the Aga Khan's Sardinian resort – I'll have to subsidise.

NOTES

Sardinian Secrets (The Times) 071 222 1267

PACKING LIST

1. JANET REGER LINGERIE
2. SUPERTAN
3. PRECAUTIONS!
4. M'S CREDIT CARD.

M	T	W	T	F	S	S	M	T	W	T	F	S	S	M	T	W	T	F	S	S
15	16	17	18	19	20	21	22	23	24	25	26	27	28	29	30	31				

15 MONDAY

Booked Sardinia through Marcus's travel Agent - told him it was for a 3 woman residential course.

16 TUESDAY

Marcus STILL sitting cross legged in the box room wearing a bed sheet! - Decide to leave him to it.

17 WEDNESDAY TO SARDINIA

Airport a nightmare - Let the cockneys run riot in Duty Free while I found the 1st Class Lounge - Lovely, handsome attentive staff - all gay, alas. On the flight was invited to join mile high club by fat, smelly businessman. Told him I was a founder member & didn't go in for sex with SLUGS!

18 THURSDAY

NOT A BAD HOTEL, but then it is £150 a night. S&T complaining about lack of fried breakfast facilities - Pretended I didn't know them and spent the morning poolside. Thought I spotted RUPERT EVERETT - but it can't be.

AUGUST 1994

M	T	W	T	F	S	S	M	T	W	T	F	S	S
1	2	3	4	5	6	7	8	9	10	11	12	13	14

FRIDAY 19

IT IS!! Rupert Everett is staying here – incognito – while learning his lines for his new film – he plays the Bad Guy in BATMAN 3!!
Told him I was an English graduate and offered to read with him....

SATURDAY 20

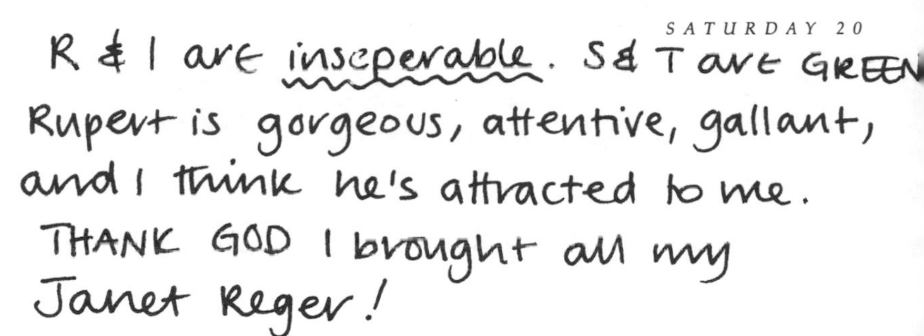

R & I are insceperable. S & T are GREEN
Rupert is gorgeous, attentive, gallant, and I think he's attracted to me.
THANK GOD I brought all my Janet Reger!

SUNDAY 21

Went for a drive in the mountains with Rupert.
Stopped his car and made WILD, PASSIONATE LOVE in an olive grove. This is the REAL THING – I KNOW IT!!

NOTES

Don't forget:
Send postcards!!

M	T	W	T	F	S	S	M	T	W	T	F	S	S	M	T	W	T	F	S	S
15	16	17	18	19	20	21	22	23	24	25	26	27	28	29	30	31				

22 MONDAY

I'M **SO** SCARED!! Rupert and I were kidnapped by Sicilian bandits. We're being held in a stinking cattleshed. For the first 5 hours we were tied together – never thought I'd object to that – BUT I DID!

23 TUESDAY

GOD! -This is the **WORST** experience of my life – and Rupert has gone to pieces. *Insists* he isn't R.E. at all, but a lookalike called Simon who gets work on commercials Rupert is too grand to do. NEVER thought Rupert would be a liar *AND* a coward!

23 WEDNESDAY

Weds: Our captors are angry. They sent a message to Sharon and Tracey saying they wanted a million dollars for us, and Sharon said 'KEEP HER!' What to do?? I'll have to make up to one of the bandits tomorrow.

25 THURSDAY

Luigi isn't too bad once you get to know him – Nothing wrong with him a bath, or shower or dentist and abstention from garlic wouldn't cure. Manage to persuade him I fancy him *MADLY*!

AUGUST 1994	M	T	W	T	F	S	S	M	T	W	T	F	S	S
	1	2	3	4	5	6	7	8	9	10	11	12	13	14

FRIDAY 26

Woke up in Luigi's sweaty grasp. Try to wipe from my memory what I HAD to do last night. Attempt to tip-toe from the room but he wakes & gets amorous. SAVED by the arrival of Italian commandoes.

SATURDAY 27

All day ALONE in bed asleep.

SUNDAY 28

Went looking for Rupert. Tracey says he's been arrested for non-payment of bills and impersonating a film-star. Not a first offence apparently.

NOTES

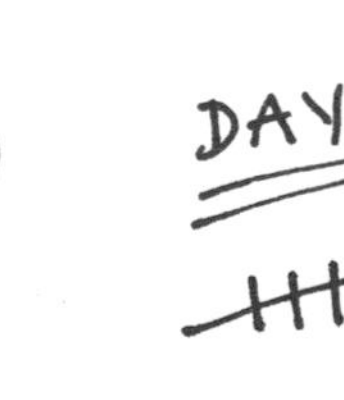

D	R
1	
1	
2	0

M	T	W	T	F	S	S	M	T	W	T	F	S	S	M	T	W	T	F	S	S
15	16	17	18	19	20	21	22	23	24	25	26	27	28	29	30	31				

29 MONDAY Bank Holiday

All day in bed ALONE - awake.

30 TUESDAY

* BACK TO UK *

End of holiday. What a delightful time - though the common slags next door enjoyed themselves well enough. Seems Sharon got off with one of the airline stewards I was convinced batted for the other side. DAMN!

31 WEDNESDAY

MARCUS HAS GIVEN UP BUDDHISM !! - and joined the Labour Party (?) He has decided our obsession with material possessions must be faced politically. He's also threatening to buy a VAUXHALL!

1 THURSDAY

My STUPID husband !!

He's only brought home a Vauxhall brochure. Why is he so interested in a CORSA? - Perhaps he thinks they throw the models in with the car. If he thinks I'm going out in a Vauxhall.....

SEPTEMBER 1994	M	T	W	T	F	S	S	M	T	W	T	F	S	S
				1	2	3	4	5	6	7	8	9	10	11

FRIDAY 2

M says he can't join the Labour Party in a Jaguar. We have a TREMENDOUS row & I go next door to S&T. Tracey is busy writing a letter to Darryl. I glance over her shoulder – no SEXY bits at all – If my man was banged up.... OH! Never mind

SATURDAY 3

Not talking to Marcus – No man at the moment.

I'm FORCED to read a book.

SUNDAY 4

Reading 'The Importance of Being Earnest'. That's funny – he says 'I never travel without my diary. One should always have something sensational to read in the train!' I agree entirely – except I NEVER travel by train. I also shan't travel by car if Marcus keeps up this mishigas with getting a Vauxhall.

NOTES

M	T	W	T	F	S	S	M	T	W	T	F	S	S	M	T	W	T	F	S	S
12	13	14	15	16	17	18	19	20	21	22	23	24	25	26	27	28	29	30		

5 MONDAY

Marcus has gone to the local Vauxhall dealers - which I ought to say is NOT in Chigwell. I think he's gone to a place called Romford(?) or some other god-forsaken backwater. If he comes home WITHOUT the Jaguar - I'M LEAVING HIM.

6 TUESDAY Rosh Hashanah

Go to Chigwell shul - see Melanie Fishman. She tells me about her new lovers - 19 year old identical twins. They feel the same things at the same time! Rabbi Shatner tells us to be quiet - 'God can hear everything we're talking about'. No wonder he's got a long white beard!!

7 WEDNESDAY

Go into S&T's - Tracey's at a prison visit. I spend an HOUR trying to explain to Sharon why buying a Vauxhall is acceptable grounds for divorce - but she can't begin to understand (??)

8 THURSDAY

M. STILL has the Jaguar - I am STILL in Bryan Close. I ask Sharon if she would take a day off and come to Romford tomorrow - I guess she would know where it is and speak in Romford's native tongue. She says - 'Blimey! whassgoindaaninRomford!!! Whatever THAT means??!

Red Herrings 0237 664823

FRIDAY 9

We go to the Vauxhall dealership – very nice salesman – GARY. Sharon fancies him, ('I could give that one!!') – but I can see he's hot for me. We test drive a CORSA – I don't like it at all. It doesn't even have leather seats! Gary then takes me for a spin in a FRONTERA.... The suspension is INFINITELY better...

SATURDAY 10

The Levitts – Lunch 12.30

IMPORTANT clients of M's – I get in a firm of caterers 'Red Herrings'. Waldo – the cook – tells me They NEARLY named a salad after him. I am about to ask if he likes being tossed when M. comes in for the corkscrew. Waldo says he will teach me ALL about slow simmering on an Aga!!...

SUNDAY 11

VISIT M'S MOTHER

She keeps asking me why we have never had children? I tell her Marcus would rather have a Vauxhall!!

NOTES

Waldo 0237 664491

Get caterers for Saturday – Try 'Red Herrings??'

M	T	W	T	F	S	S	M	T	W	T	F	S	S	M	T	W	T	F	S	S
12	13	14	15	16	17	18	19	20	21	22	23	24	25	26	27	28	29	30		

12 MONDAY I call Waldo and ask when he can show me how to simmer slowly until I come to the boil? He says he's doing a dinner party for a book publisher this Saturday, would I come along?? I would have to pretend to be a waitress — COUNT ME IN!!

13 TUESDAY M. receives membership forms for the Labour party – I think he's FLIPPED! This afternoon I start writing another chapter of my novel.
If I'm going to the house of a publisher, I might be able to slip something into his lap....

14 WEDNESDAY GARY telephones and asks if I would like to try a SENATOR. I ask which Senator he has in mind?? (Edward Kennedy always appealed to me). He means their 'top of the range' model. I say when can we test drive it? He says he could bring it over to me – I suggest 3.30 on Friday.

15 THURSDAY DINNER AT AUNTIE LILY'S – Yom Kippur
TODAY IS THE DAY OF ATONEMENT – I atone all right!! All of which I tell Melanie Fishman about. She gives out little shrieks of pleasure. Rabbi Shatner tells us to be quiet. – Tonight we go to Marcus's Auntie Lily to break our fast. I haven't let ANYTHING pass my lips all day.

M	T	W	T	F	S	S	M	T	W	T	F	S	S
			1	2	3	4	5	6	7	8	9	10	11

Cosmo 626 9472

3.30 GARY & THE SENATOR!

FRIDAY 16

What a LET DOWN! Gary brought the Senator, not bad for under £30,000. I ask if the name and hub caps can be removed. After the test drive, I ask if he would like another one... I show him what orthopaedic suspension can feel like, but as soon as I get down to the lilac silk Janet Reger, it's all too much for him!!

SATURDAY 17

DINNER PARTY WITH WALDO

Marcus asks if I would mind the Chigwell Labour Party meeting at the house - I tell him I'm going to a party so he can do what he likes as long as he uses the rubbish crockery - it seems a shame to waste Villeroy & Bosch on socialists. How many people is M. expecting? '3, including himself' - I'm surprised Chigwell can run to 3 Labour Party members!!

SUNDAY 18

* SUNDAY - WHAT A NIGHT!! Maybe the best of the year! Waldo & I simmer slowly on the Aga... he has a very nasty burn. I ask ~~the publisher if he would read my novel.~~ He says - 'Why don't I bring it to his office & read it to him??' This man has STYLE!

NOTES

M	T	W	T	F	S	S	M	T	W
12	13	14	15	16	17	18	19	20	21

HOT STUFF!

UNIFORM Supplies
0457 927356
Do you wear a uniform?
We can supply all sizes, shapes and styles... from French Maid to Lance Corporal.

19 MONDAY

Waldo in hospital – Second degree burns apparently.

20 TUESDAY M. to Vienna on business – Back Sat. Tracey asks if I would help arrange a surprise party for Sharon. I say I know a VERY GOOD caterer... When is S's birthday? September 30th – She's a Virgo (some hopes!) Why does T want to plan it now? 'Because she has to save up' – save up?? – the working classes have some very strange habits. I agree to help.

Sukkot Begins

21 WEDNESDAY

Off to see COSMO ORBEN – the publisher.

22 THURSDAY Good thing Marcus is away on business!! – I didn't get home until 7 this morning.
Cosmo publishes a book on the Marquis de Sade and we act out the first three chapters – FIVE to go.....!

FRIDAY 23

I telephone a 'certain' video club and ask if they have a movie entitled 'POPE INNOCENT XV' – strongly recommended by Cosmo. It'll come on a pizza motorcycle (Chigwell's answer to a brown paper bag) tomorrow.

SATURDAY 24

M. returns Austria.

Watch the video about this Pope with very strong, chunky thighs and three housewives with broken dishwashers! Oh! and there's a LOT more. Marcus comes home from Vienna – I suggest

SUNDAY 25

we go STRAIGHT to bed! He thinks this is a good idea as he has had a rotten journey from Austria.
I want bizarre sex,
M. wants to tell me he's been made Deputy Chairman of the Chigwell LABOUR party!!

certain
VIDEO CLUB
16 High Street
Chigwell
9894
☆ AMAZING NEW TITLES
☆ EXCELLENT VALUE
☆ OPEN ALL DAY, EVERY DAY
☆ MAKE SURE YOU'RE certain...
No: 5724

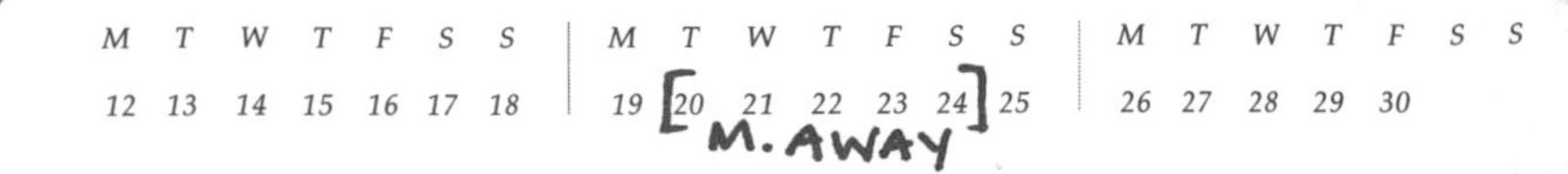

'The Zulu Warriors' 422 4216

26 MONDAY

Melanie comes over to ask if I would be interested in SWAPPING Cosmo for identical twins??

27 TUESDAY Tracey pops in. She's anxious about Sharon's surprise party. I tell her I will ask Cosmo what he thinks would be a good idea – T. thought a male strippergram might be a good laugh... Do I know anyone? HONESTLY??

28 WEDNESDAY Tracey is FRANTIC about Sharon's party. I tell her I've been given the name of a very UNUSUAL catering firm. I call and speak to a man called INNES. He takes my address & the time I shall be in.... alone – tomorrow.

10.30 Innes

29 THURSDAY Innes comes around. His firm, THE ZULU WARRIORS, specialize in African cuisine. Where they differ from other outfits like Jewish catering firms is all the waiters are men, NAKED MEN. Choose 4. Innes tells me a selection of dips will take on a whole new meaning at this party!!

OCTOBER 1994

M	T	W	T	F	S	S	M	T	W	T	F	S	S
31					1	2	3	4	5	6	7	8	9

SHARON'S BIRTHDAY FRIDAY 30

I go in at about 9 & give her a 2 month subscription to Weight Watchers which M. & I thought was rather apt. I also give her a very rude card which says....'Big, Black & Beautiful'- Sharon says she wouldn't mind waking up next to him!! -Isn't she in for a SURPRISE.... !!

SATURDAY 1

Last night T. took S. to the wine bar, S didn't want to go, T. insisted, they rowed, walked into Datentrace and there were 20 friends (most of them common oiks from N. London who one shouldn't really encourage to come to Chigwell), and 4 waiters....naked, except for bowler hats. The night went with a BANG!..... for me & Carlton!

SUNDAY 2

Wear some seriously sexy underwear and book a taxi to Cosmo's house. Tonight we are - apparently - reading excerpts from 'In Praise of Panty Hose' by Sabina Sedgewick. There will be 9 of us - 7 MEN & 2 WOMEN!!

NOTES

ORDER SOME V. SPICY DIPS FROM THE CATERERS

M	T	W	T	F	S	S	M	T	W	T	F	S	S	M	T	W	T	F	S	S
10	11	12	13	14	15	16	17	18	19	20	21	22	23	24	25	26	27	28	29	30

3 MONDAY Just in case this diary ever falls into the wrong hands – it's better I don't record what I actually did last night... Met 'Vernon', a prominent Tory MP, at the reading. He invited me to the House of Commons for lunch. I won't say who he is, but I'd know him naked!!!

4 TUESDAY M. gets Vauxhall Corsa. They do a tremendous range of colours, I have to say. M. chooses grey – typical of the man. Cosmo would have gone for a shocking pink. We are keeping the Jaguar. M says I can drive it.

5 WEDNESDAY M. is invited as a delegate to the Labour Party Conference. Who is he a delegate of?? The National Union of Jewish Chartered Accountants and Ulcer Sufferers??

6 THURSDAY Melanie comes over. Tell her – in STRICTEST confidence, all about the literary circle, Sabina Sedgewick and her novel. Melanie is GREEN with envy – I have her eating out of my hand.

M	T	W	T	F	S	S	M	T	W	T	F	S	S
31					1	2	3	4	5	6	7	8	9

M.P.!!

FRIDAY 7

Sharon comes in and says Cosmo is on the phone. Well – I couldn't give him *my* home number, could I??

SATURDAY 8

Cosmo is acting as inter-mediary for 'Vernon' and invites me to go to Prime Minister's Question Time on 13th. 'Vernon' thinks I could go down very well on/in Conservative circles!!

SUNDAY 9

Cosmo asks if I would like to join '*CLITS*'-Charleston Literary and IntellecTual society-Apparently Charleston was where the Bloomsbury Set used to hang out. I say 'count me in'... but Cosmo says I have to be interviewed for membership. Could I attend his home?? – Can a fish swim??

NOTES

M	T	W	T	F	S	S	M	T	W	T	F	S	S	M	T	W	T	F	S	S
10	11	12	13	14	15	16	17	18	19	20	21	22	23	24	25	26	27	28	29	30

10 MONDAY CLITS Tell M. I'm going to the Jewish Women's Guild. He asks if I'm happily married? I tell him I can't talk now, I'll be late for my meeting. He wants to talk about our marriage, I can go to the JWG any time – NOT THIS Women's Guild I can't! I leave him & drive to Holland Park.

11 TUESDAY – WHAT A NIGHT!!

M. asks why the JWG at a local shul should go on until 2.30am? – I tell him he shouldn't bother with trivialities. 'I love you,' I tell him. He gets all maudlin and says how lucky he is to have me. I tell him not now – it's been a long, hard night!!

12 WEDNESDAY

I've been invited to the Conservative Party Conference in Brighton!!! I'm booked into the GRAND!

13 THURSDAY PM'S QT – Drive to Westminster. 'Vernon' takes me to the Strangers Bar. I am introduced to people who are better left unnamed. Sit through PM's Question Time and all through it I can see a particular MP smiling up at me – HE'S GOT TO BE JOKING!!!

M	T	W	T	F	S	S	M	T	W	T	F	S	S
31					1	2	3	4	5	6	7	8	9

FRIDAY 14

M. is worried - last night he split the Chigwell Labour Party and a prominent member resigned - Then there were 2.... And <u>still</u> Marcus can't become Chairman!!

SATURDAY 15

M. drinks too much & starts preaching to me why the Tories are bringing this country to it's knees. I say 'I hope they bring me to my knees in Brighton...' but M. is too sozzled to hear what I said.

SUNDAY 16

DINNER AT MELANIE'S. Fishman's for dinner - Melanie's husband, Charles, & Marcus are thinking of going into business together. Charles asks M. what he can put up? I am about to blurt

NOTES

out the answer but why should I ruin M's chances <u>and</u> embarrass him at the same time??

0273 30512
The Grand Hotel
Brighton
Suite 476
19.10. → ?

M	T	W	T	F	S	S	M	T	W	T	F	S	S	M	T	W	T	F	S	S
10	11	12	13	14	15	16	17	18	19	20	21	22	23	24	25	26	27	28	29	30

Pick up video for Melanie.

OCTOBER 1994

17 MONDAY Tory party conference begins today. I am going down on Wednesday until Friday. Cosmo is driving me. He has a FERRARI. I've asked him to collect me from Melanie Fishman's – just to see her face!!

18 TUESDAY

Melanie asks when she can meet Cosmo? I lend her the video 'Pope Innocent XV' which I copied from VHS to Betamax – ALL Jews have Betamax!

[WE]DNESDAY TO BRIGHTON ..... (Melanie's 10.00)

OFF TO THE CONFERENCE! My suite is next door to Cecil Parkinson .... IS THIS SAFE??

94
[CONS]ERVATIVE
[CON]FERENCE
[Gr]een

[THU]RSDAY Attend debates in the Conference Hall, but this Tory Party is too liberal for me. Of course one has to vote for them, there is no other party! EVENING: I'm discreetly ushered into a private party. Have a very interesting conversation with Kenneth Clarke, but conversation is where it stops. I couldn't fancy him BAKED!!

OCTOBER 1994

M	T	W	T	F	S	S	M	T	W	T	F	S	S
31					1	2	3	4	5	6	7	8	9

FRIDAY 21

HEAVY night with some big knobs.. in The Party, rather hungover. Bump into Lady Thatcher in the Ladies – we have a chat about being married to men who pale into insignificance when we're around. This evening is the Conservative Party Ball – and I'm going with Cosmo – decoy for 'Vernon' – SO EXCITING

SATURDAY 22

SAT:– Phone M. to tell him I'll be late. Don't mention the Conference as M. is a dyed-in the-wool Socialist, STUPIDMAN! The Ball was wonderful although I couldn't cast my spell over Michael Portillo (DAMN!) 'Vernon' took me to an alternative Ball afterwards & for discretion's sake I can only say that 'Ball' was the operative word.

SUNDAY 23

British Summer Time ends

SUNDAY: Visit Charleston – Delightful. Virginia Woolf & her sister came here under the pretence of writing & painting, but really they used to have WILD parties. 'Vernon' Cosmo, 1 or 2 other Tories, and little old me re-enacted a typical weekend – 3 line whip takes on a whole new meaning!!

NOTES

M	T	W	T	F	S	S	M	T	W	T	F	S	S	M	T	W	T	F	S	S
10	11	12	13	14	15	16	17	18	19	20	21	22	23	24	25	26	27	28	29	30

BRIGHTON

24 MONDAY massage 3.30pm — United Nations Day

Arrived home LATE last night.

25 TUESDAY

Telephone rings... It's Waldo – the chef. He's had to have some skin removed from his bicep & grafted onto his right buttock. The Aga burn was really quite serious!!

26 WEDNESDAY EMPIRE 7.30 PM

M. invited to the ROYAL CHARITY PREMIER of a new film. It's at the Empire, Leicester square. When I say 'Royal', it isn't really Royal: it's only Prince Edward!

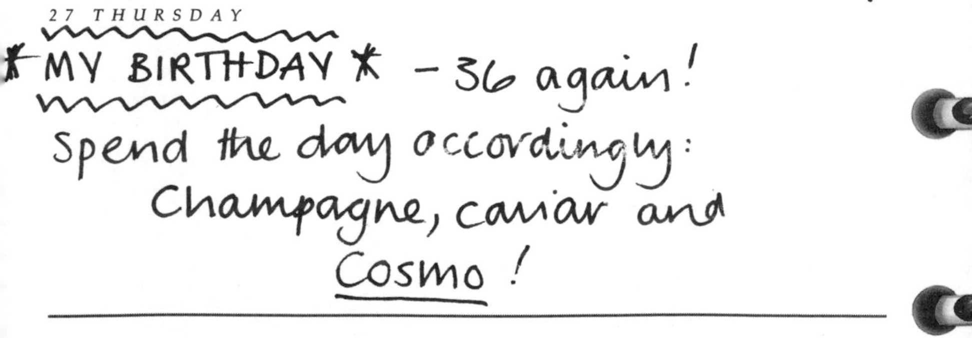

27 THURSDAY

* MY BIRTHDAY * – 36 again!

Spend the day accordingly: Champagne, caviar and Cosmo!

FRIDAY 28

CLITS 8PM A Junior Minister asks if he can drive my car home – WHY NOT?? We are stopped, he's breathalysed – the crystals turn fluorescent!! Thankfully I'm Jewish & don't drink anything stronger than cherry brandy!!

SATURDAY 29

The M.P. who must remain nameless, is charged with DRUNKEN DRIVING. I phone him – He says the story mustn't get out. Oh, a political scandal! – NEVER been involved in one of those before. That's one in the eye for Melanie Fishman!

SUNDAY 30

I buy ALL the papers and check the front pages. The Mirror have it: "Minister & Mystery Lady(!) in Drink Drive Adventure". How did they get the story??

...are unable to comm... ...dispute ...l will not ...radley (49), Mr. Bradley has promised the will try to have everything in the

MINISTER AND MYSTERY LADY IN DRINK DRIVE ...TURE

Brad Conway 081 936 2476

OCTOBER / NOVEMBER

31 MONDAY Receive an anonymous call to go to a West Ham public house – it's 'vitally important.' Sounds intriguing! I find the pub and the anonymous caller finds me. He says he's here on the Minister's behalf. I have to stand up in court & say I was driving or the Minister's career could be over.....

October Holiday (R. of Ireland)

1 TUESDAY This is SO thrilling – who can I tell? Tracey is the only person who would keep it to herself. I find her under the sink trying to repair a leak – How unladylike. I ask if I could have a word. She asks me if I would like her plunger up some part of my anatomy I couldn't identify.!!

2 WEDNESDAY M. & I to Leicester Square for film Premier

The Slaughtered Lamb (!!)
6, Nile Street
2.30pm

3 THURSDAY

The film was DREADFUL – the party was FANTASTIC. Prince Edward's detective showed a lot of interest. Perhaps he can help me out of my dilemma?? Stupid Marcus only tries to 'chat up' some bimbo. Who does he think he is? The director asked if I'd ever thought of acting?? I take his number......

NOVEMBER 1994	M	T	W	T	F	S	S	M	T	W	T	F	S	S
		1	2	3	4	5	6	7	8	9	10	11	12	13

FRIDAY 4

Should I call Brad - the director?? Was he serious?? I find him strangely attractive. His girlfriend was VERY wary of me - she knows a challenge when she sees it.

SATURDAY 5

The anonymous caller calls again - I tell him I can't own up to driving the Minister. He tells me I'll be sorry....

SUNDAY 6

SLEEPLESS NIGHT.... I must tell Marcus. I suggest dinner this evening - M. knows there's something wrong.

NOTES

M	T	W	T	F	S	S	M	T	W	T	F	S	S	M	T	W	T	F	S	S
14	15	16	17	18	19	20	21	22	23	24	25	26	27	28	29	30				

7 MONDAY I tell M. I've joined a respectable Literary Circle (he was pleased). I tell him I was being driven home by a member, a male member (he was wary). I tell him the male member is an MP (he was curious). I tell him the MP is a Tory (he was angry). Then I tell him the MP was over the limit and now the Press want to know who he was driving home – Then the bill arrived – (he was APOPLECTIC!).

8 TUESDAY

TUESDAY

Two papers run with the story. The Minister's wife has left him – He will probably have to resign – OH MY GOD!!

9 WEDNESDAY M. TO MILAN M. dashes into the bedroom!! – There are photographers ALL over our front lawn!! M. panics! Fat lot of good he is! S & T come in. Sharon says the photographers are 'lowering the tone of the area!' THAT'S RICH – coming from her.

10 THURSDAY

Photographers EVERYWHERE! Sharon suggests she be a decoy, so I can sneak out and get to Wax Factor. I am grossly insulted that Sharon thinks anyone would mistake her for me... but, it works! I come out of the 'Tradesmans entrance' for the 1st time since ~~I've lived in Chigwell & catch a bus!!~~ (for the 1st time since I've been married!)

FRIDAY 11

I lie low and keep
Shtum.
(I think that's the word ??).

SATURDAY 12

The DAILY MAIL call. They know I'm the 'other' woman in the scandal. Who tipped them off? They offer me £25,000 to 'spill the beans'. What a vulgar vocabulary.

Rememberance Sunday

SUNDAY 13

- Pop in on S & T for advice - they both say I should 'kiss and tell'. But NOTHING happened between me and the Minister! Sharon says I'm making it up!

NOTES

M	T	W	T	F	S	S	M	T	W	T	F	S	S	M	T	W	T	F	S	S
14	15	16	17	18	19	20	21	22	23	24	25	26	27	28	29	30				

14 MONDAY M. BACK – I tell him about the cash offer. He says it isn't worth it: 'After tax you would only be left with £17,000; then there are the expenses: travel, new clothes for photographs....' I'll phone the Mail tomorrow.

15 TUESDAY

Tory Party Central Office make me a counter offer. I tell them nothing happened but they insist they know the Minister's reputation and have wanted to get rid of him for some time, they just need proof!

16 WEDNESDAY

Murdo has landed a job as a gardener in FRANCE. He needs references and has come over to ask if I would give him one. I tell him I'd love to but I can't remember just how good he was – it was a long time ago......

17 THURSDAY

I give Murdo a 3 page reference.

FRIDAY 18

M. asks why, if nothing went on between me and the Minister, should the Mail have offered me £25,000 and Tory Party Central Office want to bribe me? I look him in the eye and ask the all-important question: 'Do you think I would EVER be unfaithful to you, darling?' M. says 'of course not'

SATURDAY 19

Lunch with the Tories tomorrow. M says I should ask them to double the Mail offer. After all, he said, they can afford it! (Is this the end of his silly Socialist flirtation?? I HOPE so.)

SUNDAY 20

LUNCH 1.00 – WHAT a meeting! I have never been so scared in my life! I told them I wanted £50,000 – they told me what I could do. They said they have photographs in their possession.... The gentlemen, who never once told me his name, said 'I think we understand each other...'

maybe I should keep a low profile. →

M	T	W	T	F	S	S	M	T
14	15	16	17	18	19	20	21	22

21 MONDAY

VERY FRUSTRATED

In more than one sense.

22 TUESDAY 'VERNON' doesn't answer my calls Cosmo is in New York .... permanently, and when I ask Mif he'd like a jacuzzi he says all that swirling water makes his appendix rumble! WHAT do I have to do to get my husband in the mood???

23 WEDNESDAY JD&S? Pop in on S&T. I ask if they'd like to go to a Jewish divorced and separated evening in Barkingside. Tracey says she isn't divorced - I point out she's separated.

24 THURSDAY WHAT A BUNCH OF LOSERS!! A dentist called Alan picks me up. A shoe salesman called Benny tries to pick up Tracey, until she tells him she's not Jewish; and a taxi driver called Martin tries to pick up Sharon - and gets a hernia!!

M	T	W	T	F	S	S	M	T	W	T	F	S	S
	1	2	3	4	5	6	7	8	9	10	11	12	13

FRIDAY 25

Walking past an Estate Agents I see Luke inside. Do I go in? Can one recapture the past?? I invite him out for a drink 'for old time's sake'. I suggest my place. He thinks we should go somewhere safer. I suggest <u>his</u> place.

SATURDAY 26

ALAN the dentist phones me ... AT HOME!! How did he get my number? Sharon gave it to him. He asks if I would like to go out next Sunday?? Martin has invited Sharon & perhaps we could make it a foursome – a foursome with Sharon?? <u>EUGH</u>!!

SUNDAY 27

7.00 LUKE

LUKE – the man who made my body work like no other before <u>OR</u> since, except Murdo .... or Cosmo .... Waldo took some beating. And what about the gorgeous Kenelm? No, all right, there <u>have</u> been others as good as Luke, but Luke was special...

NOTES

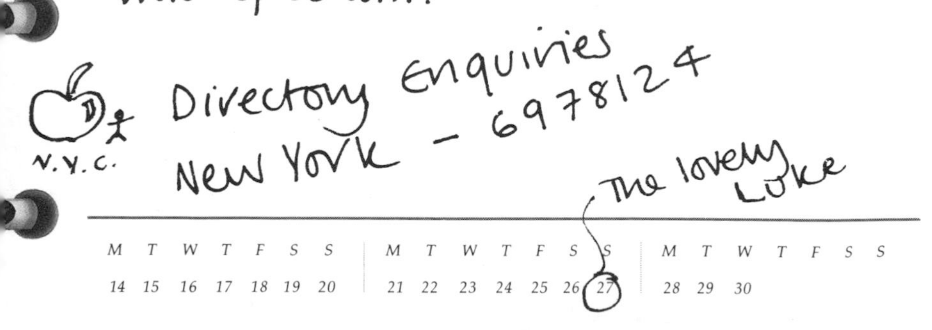

28 MONDAY LUKE IS FREE! – His engagement to the SLUT, Carmen, is over. I suggest we try again, but he says only if I leave Marcus. Luke says he earns enough to keep us both. Does the boy know how much I cost??

29 TUESDAY Ask S&T for advice. T. says marriage is forever and I shouldn't be strumping other men. S. says I should give Marcus the heave-ho, what have I got to lose? I explain that there's the house; the Jaguar; the allowance; the 10 holidays a year; the charge accounts...

30 WEDNESDAY St Andrew

Phone Marcus and ask if we can meet tomorrow for lunch? I want to discuss the future. He suggests meeting by Marble Arch, buying some sandwiches & sitting in Hyde Park. I suggest Le Caprice.

1 THURSDAY LE CAPRICE 1.00 PM ~ I see Nigel Havers. We smile. We don't know each other, but that could be arranged... M. arrives. I ask where our marriage is going? He doesn't understand. Just as I'm explaining, his portable cellnet goes and he has to leave.

DECEMBER 1994	M	T	W	T	F	S	S	M	T	W	T	F	S	S
				1	2	3	4	5	6	7	8	9	10	11

FRIDAY 2

M. & I talk. He loves me, couldn't live without me.... 'Why don't you ever make mad, passionate love to me,' I ask. He asks what I mean. I'm married to a KLUTZ!! 'You couldn't be unfaithful to me, could you, Dolly?' He says. I say OF COURSE NOT(!!), but a woman has needs...

SATURDAY 3

Luke phones. He says if I don't leave Marcus by Tuesday, he's giving up his job and going to New York. I decide to leave Marcus – But how can I tell him??

SUNDAY 4

The atmosphere between M. and myself is strained. M's cousin Sidney & Kitty come to Lunch. I cook – salmon, asparagus, Beluga caviar, the normal. I drink too much and tell Kitty I'm leaving M. She says she and Sidney expected it years ago!!

NOTES

WAYS TO TELL MARCUS:

1. Tell Sharon.
2. Tell his mother.
3. With flowers??

M	T	W	T	F	S	S	M	T	W	T	F	S	S	M	T	W	T	F	S	S
12	13	14	15	16	17	18	19	20	21	22	23	24	25	26	27	28	29	30	31	

5 MONDAY HAIRCUT 10·00 HOW can I give up this lifestyle?? Perhaps I'm not a one man woman..... I discuss my dilemma with Deke, my hairdresser. He says if I run off with Luke, guys like Duncan, his DISHY new junior, would be out of bounds... This DOES it. No one man can be worth

6 TUESDAY the many I would be tossing away.

I tell LUKE I can't run away with him. I am in TEARS! Then Duncan comes to wax my legs. I tell him to be gentle. He's 19 and when he touches my hair, let alone my legs.... PHEW!!

7 WEDNESDAY Yesterday Tracey came to borrow my lawnmower - and.... she REALLY fancies Duncan. Wonders never cease?!! I tell Duncan not to hold his breath, she is absolutely faithful - AND her husband is a dangerous criminal. We resume the leg waxing - Then my bikini line. Then.... 19 year olds have

8 THURSDAY SUCH stamina.

Take Mummy to lunch. We see Michael Caine and she asks for his autograph. I could have DIED!! HOW EMBARRASSING!!! Then Mummy tells me Sidney has told M. I'm leaving him!! OH NO!

FRIDAY 9

SAVAGE row with M. He asks if there's someone else – I tell him there is no ONE else. In bed M. tries to be passionate, but I fall asleep. M says 'Why can't it always be like this?' LIKE WHAT?? M. books us on the Orient Express to Venice. This is the most romantic thing he has done whilst I've kept awake!!

SATURDAY 10

→ VENICE

Sat – 10 minutes out of Dover and M. is sick. What a klutz!! We board the train in Boulogne and he takes to his bottom bunk – (afraid of heights). Dinner with an Italian called Flavia (30 & travelling alone). My lucky weekend or what?!?

SUNDAY 11

6.00am – Wake up in the top bunk with Flavia!! (I am not afraid of heights). Back to my cabin to find Marcus so white he clashes with the sheets. The old hypochondriac. MILAN STATION – Flavia asks if I would run off with him. We run off back to his cabin. MAMMA MIA!!!

NOTES

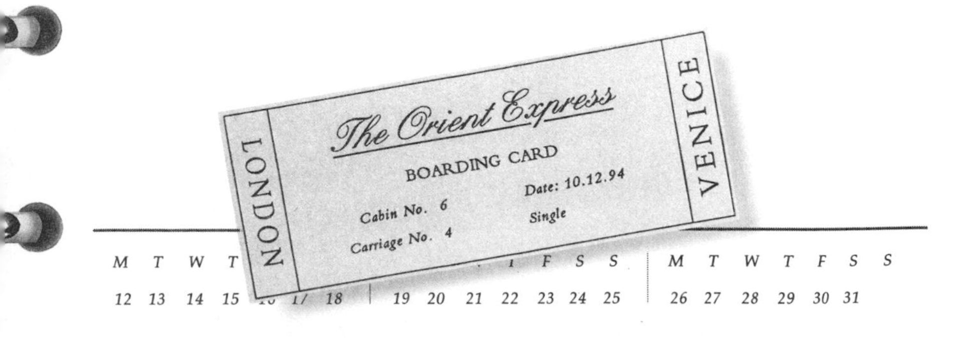

M	T	W	T	F	S	S	M	T	W	T	F	S	S	M	T	W	T	F	S	S
12	13	14	15	16	17	18	19	20	21	22	23	24	25	26	27	28	29	30	31	

12 MONDAY VENICE – M. takes a turn for the worse. Flavia and I take a Gondola and steal more than a kiss under the Rialto (those hands... that tongue!). He says 'why don't we spend our last night in the Cipriani?' Isn't this where Heseltine had his heart attack??

13 TUESDAY FLY BACK TO LONDON. M. doesn't stop apologising for ruining my weekend!! Sharon pops in. Tracey's birthday is next Tuesday and would I keep the evening free to go to T's favourite pub in Hoxton? Can't wait – Where's Hoxton??

14 WEDNESDAY

Melanie has won 2 days for 2 at a Health farm in a Jewish charity raffle. COUNT ME IN! She's green about Flavia – She's never had an Italian. I ask M. if he minds me going with Melanie? He says of course not, I deserve a break after he ruined my time on the Orient Express. BLESS HIM!

15 THURSDAY Sharon asks where I'm going with Melanie and can she come with! Mind you, she needs a Health farm more than me do. We arrive and immediately set our sights on Indian doctors, Saeed and Vishram. They ask if we would like mixed doubles this afternoon – Tennis??

Vishram
room 369

FRIDAY 16

The boys think we are great fun – which we are. We have a sauna together and a roll in the snow. Spend the evening on the squash court with Vishram. All that banging against the walls gives me an appetite – I really fancy an Indian...

SATURDAY 17

Ask Vishram what he's doing ~~tomorrow~~ night – He's going to the Temple:- it's the Martyrdom of Guru Tegh Bahadur. Of course, should have known! No sign of Melanie – her car's still in the car park, so I ask reception for the keys and drive home. I like her Aston Martin. It would make a wonderful Christmas present.

SUNDAY 18

Melanie comes to collect her car. I ask about last night, she just smiles. I know what that means!!

We've both lost weight, but then we've taken PLENTY of exercise. I should send Tracey to the Health farm as a birthday present.

NOTES

THINGS TO PACK:

- Tennis racquet
- All in one black exercise catsuit.
- Lycra g-string (leopard print one & gold one)
- Trainers

M	T	W	T	F	S	S	M	T	W	T	F	S	S	M	T	W	T	F	S	S
12	13	14	15	16	17	18	19	20	21	22	23	24	25	26	27	28	29	30	31	

19 MONDAY Book T.'s birthday present. Go to Harrods - Xmas shopping: spend £4000. Buy an 18-carat-gold Aston Martin key ring. See if Marcus takes the hint. For Sharon a box of chocolates and Yardley's perfume. For Tracey a British Rail season ticket to the prison of her choice.

20 TUESDAY *TRACEY'S BIRTHDAY* - she's in a foul mood. Darryl's in solitary confinement for 3 days. What can you expect with this class of person? Lunch with Melanie: ask what happened between her and Saeed?.... It'll make a marvellous new chapter for my book!

21 WEDNESDAY M's company Christmas Party
I HATE these affairs. The lower orders mix with directors like old friends. I dance with Elvis from the photocopying room. Something comes between us.... It isn't a member of staff, but it could be the staff of a member of staff!!

22 THURSDAY
Elvis asked if I was interested in the new colour copier. The next thing I know we're locked in the photocopying room with copies of my bare bottom spurting out of the machine - It was a race to see who finished last - Elvis or the copier!!

DECEMBER 1994	M	T	W	T	F	S	S	M	T	W	T	F	S	S
				1	2	3	4	5	6	7	8	9	10	11

"DING DONG"!!

FRIDAY 22

'Last minute' Christmas shop. Ring Fortnums and ask how large is their largest Christmas Hamper? They do a Christmas and New Year Survival Hamper for only £875.00 – plus free delivery. I place my order.

SATURDAY 24

PARTY – 8pm – ANOTHER office party: Elvis takes me up to the roof. It's snowing and all I've got on is my ivory mink. I ask to go inside but some joker has locked the doors – we can't even call the police.... well, we can, but they won't hear us 19 floors up.

SUNDAY 25

Christmas Day → HAPPY CHRISTMAS!!

'Ding, Dong merrily on high....' Finally let out by security man – home at 3.30am. Tell M. I was doing intensive work for 'Save The Children'. 'You've SUCH a big-hearted person,' he says. We go to bed and he asks why I've got 'Merry Xmas' written in lipstick on my bum?? – I'll MURDER that Elvis...

NOTES

M	T	W	T	F	S	S	M	T	W	T	F	S	S	M	T	W	T	F	S	S
12	13	14	15	16	17	18	19	20	21	22	23	24	25	26	27	28	29	30	31	

 Bi 071 697 2424

26 MONDAY

Boxing Day Holiday (UK)
St. Stephen's Day Holiday (R. of Ireland)

M. not talking to me and he hasn't given me an Aston Martin - schnorrer!! He hasn't given me ANY present. At least S&T buy me a year's subscription to a male equivalent of Penthouse - bedtime reading, they say. I don't read at bedtime - I perform at bedtime.

27 TUESDAY *THE LEVYS - 7.30pm*

Bank Holiday (UK and R. of Ireland)

M. apologises and gives me my present - 'Diana Her Story'. Is he trying to tell me something? Meet THOMAS, a dermatologist, at the Levy's party. I see Marcus trying to flirt with the hostess so Thomas and I go to one of the 6 loos, lock the door and I show him a rash I keep getting...

28 WEDNESDAY

A quiet day in bed reading my magazine. Where do they find these men? Why can't I find them? Sharon says they aren't really built like this, they've been touched up. 'By whom,' I ask? - That's a job I wouldn't mind getting my hands dirty for.

29 THURSDAY It's been a quiet year really but I've had some fun. If only I could tell Marcus. If only I was brave enough to be a single woman again. NO! It's more fun being married, everything is heightened at the thought of getting found out. The problem is.... M. is NEVER likely to find out.

JANUARY 1995

M	T	W	T	F	S	S	M	T	W	T	F	S	S
30	31					1	2	3	4	5	6	7	8

MELANIE'S 8pm

FRIDAY 30

Is Thomas to be my last man of '94? This evening Marcus and I are invited to Melanie Fishman's New Year's Eve Party...

* 1995 *

Sat 1st Jan

At midnight we sing 'Auld Lang Syne' and I stand in Melanie's new kitchen and make my New Year's resolutions:

- I won't spend more than £4000 on any single garment;
- I am going to attempt to get Tracey laid this year finally
- I mustn't be unfaithful to Marcus. He's a good man really and I'm very lucky to have him as a husband.

...And then I see Melanie's brother-in-law, Braham. Now that would be a good way to start 1995. He gives me his telephone number... Must buy a new filofax.

me at Melanie's party - Hello 1995!

SUNDAY 1

NOTES

M	T	W	T	F	S	S	M	T	W	T	F	S	S	M	T	W	T	F	S	S
9	10	11	12	13	14	15	16	17	18	19	20	21	22	23	24	25	26	27	28	29

2 MONDAY *POST CHRISTMAS SESSION AT GYM*

3 TUESDAY

4 WEDNESDAY

5 THURSDAY MARCUS'S MOTHER FOR DINNER 6.30

M	T	W	T	F	S	S
						1
2	3	4	5	6	7	8

TELEPHONE NUMBERS
TELEGRAPH

TELEPHONE NUMBERS
TELEGRAPH

TELEPHONE NUMBERS

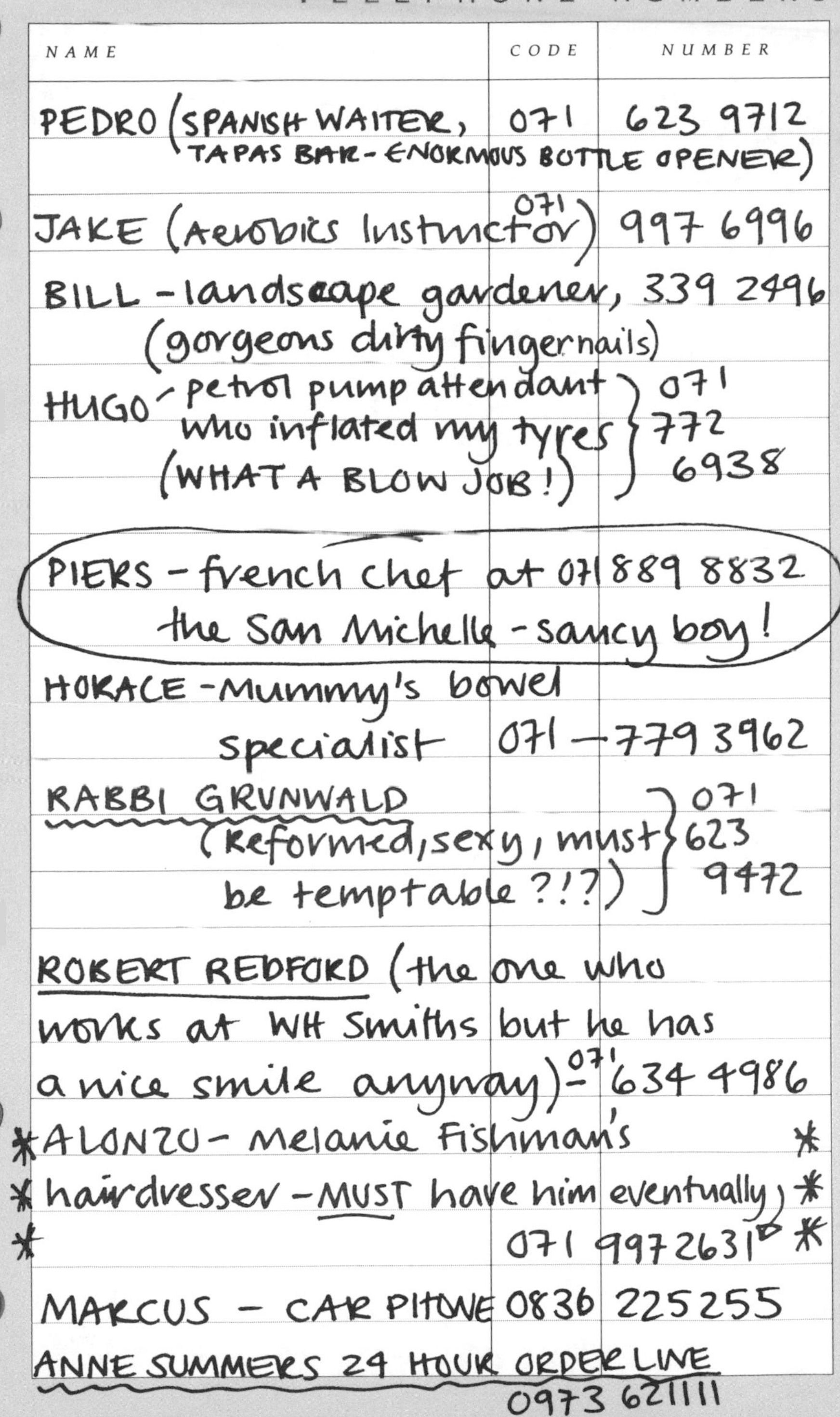

NAME	CODE	NUMBER
PEDRO (SPANISH WAITER, TAPAS BAR - ENORMOUS BOTTLE OPENER)	071	623 9712
JAKE (Aerobics Instructor)	071	997 6996
BILL - landscape gardener, (gorgeous dirty fingernails)		339 2496
HUGO - petrol pump attendant who inflated my tyres (WHAT A BLOW JOB!)	071	772 6938
PIERS - french chef at the San Michelle - saucy boy!	071	889 8832
HORACE - Mummy's bowel specialist	071	779 3962
RABBI GRUNWALD (Reformed, sexy, must be temptable ?!?)	071	623 9472
ROBERT REDFORD (the one who works at WH Smiths but he has a nice smile anyway)	071	634 4986
* ALONZO - Melanie Fishman's hairdresser - MUST have him eventually *	071	997 2631
MARCUS - CAR PHONE	0836	225255
ANNE SUMMERS 24 HOUR ORDER LINE	0973	621111

TELEPHONE NUMBERS

NAME	CODE	NUMBER
DEKE - my hairdresser - lovely but camp as a row of pink tents - MUST get him off with Melanie		911 6263
George McTaggart - hypnotherapist (sexy if aloof)	0297	9121166
→ MUMMY	071	998 9916
MRS PEARSON, my dear old cleaner.... she means well	071	992 8413
TROY, mobile masseur (lovely supple fingers)		767 6677
SINGLES - 24 hour chat line	0898	987 654
* SVEN in Sweden c/o Wing Command		400 835
ODDS & SODS SERVICES very handy around the house!	071	852 9210
VITS-R-US - Vitamins Delivery Line —	081	860 0695
Topsy Turvy Wine Bar	081	240 1467
HOUSE of COMMONS - (ask for 'Vernon') Direct Line —	071	199 3939

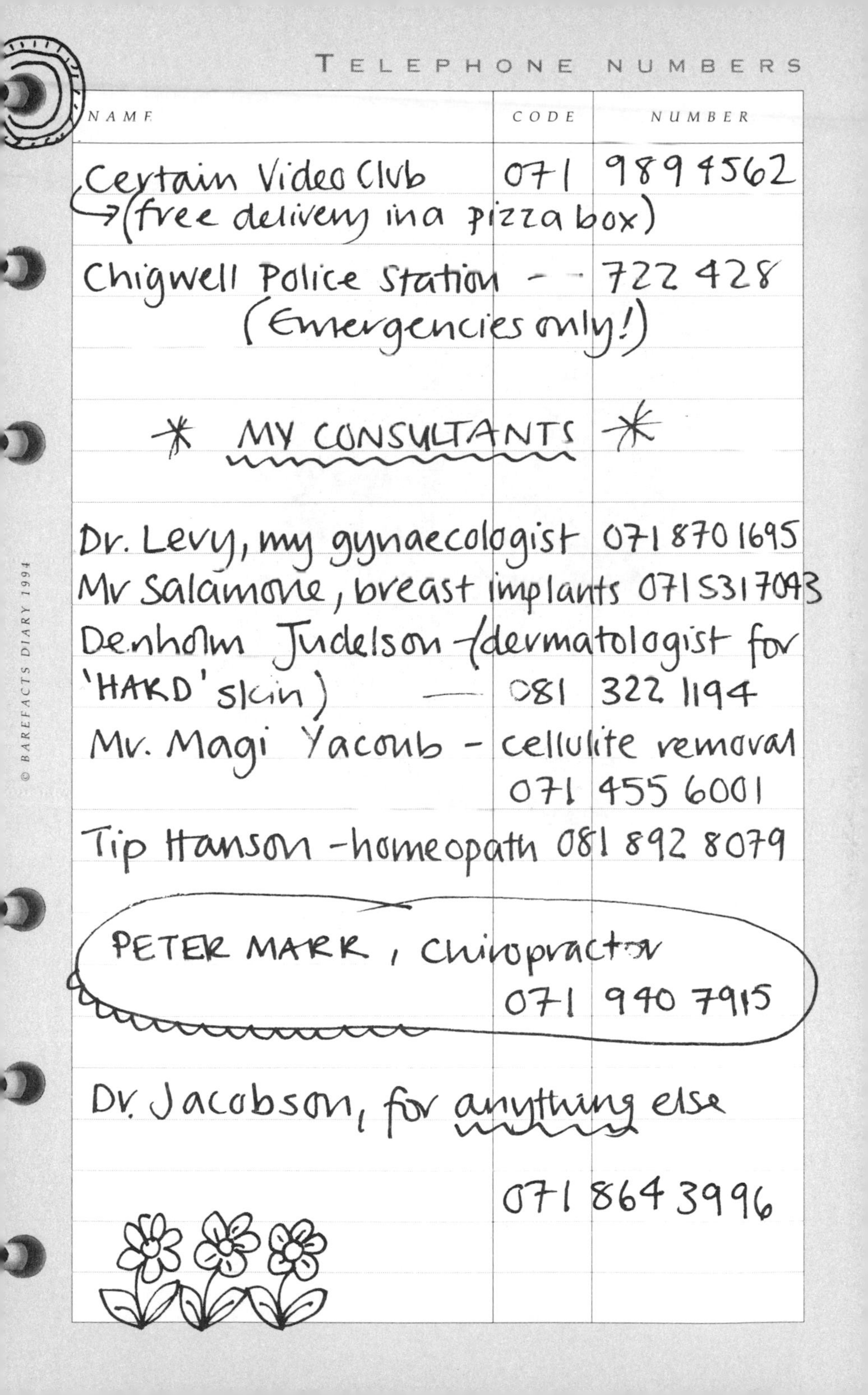

Telephone Numbers

NAME	CODE	NUMBER
Certain Video Club	071	989 4562
(free delivery in a pizza box)		
Chigwell Police Station —	—	722 428
(Emergencies only!)		
* MY CONSULTANTS *		
Dr. Levy, my gynaecologist	071	870 1695
Mr Salamone, breast implants	071	531 7043
Denholm Judelson (dermatologist for 'HARD' skin) —	081	322 1194
Mr. Magi Yacoub – cellulite removal	071	455 6001
Tip Hanson – homeopath	081	892 8079
PETER MARK, Chiropractor	071	940 7915
Dr. Jacobson, for anything else	071	864 3996

TELEPHONE NUMBERS

PERSONAL FINANCES

PERSONAL EXPENSES
DATE
ITEM
TOTAL EXPENSES
RECEIPTS
BALANCE
TOTAL
© BAREFACTS DIARY 1994
FOR DORIEN GREEN'S EYES ONLY

PERSONAL EXPENSES

DATE	ITEM	TOTAL EXPENSES	RECEIPTS	BALANCE
JANUARY	Harrods Sale - French Lingerie	544.00		
	French deli home delivery - Gross of French sticks	75.00	CLOTHES:	
	Marks & Spencer	143.00		
	Busybee dry-cleaners (persistent grass stains)	194.00	35.00	
	COLOUR CONSULTATION	1904.00	2750.00	
	TOP SHOP - (REMEMBER TO CUT OUT THE LABELS)	50.00	544.00	
	KNICKERBOX	35.00	50.00	
	IRONING SERVICE	£19.00	3,379.00	
	Mrs Pearson	15.00		
	TROY'S HOME MASSAGE (£20 TIP - WHAT A TROJAN HORSE)	48.00		
	150 PLANTS (MURDO SAYS I'VE GREEN FINGERS - I can make ANYTHING GROW!)			579.00
	HARRODS - FIORICCI DRESS	2750.00		
	MR SALAMONE - consultation for breast enlargement	£200.00	(£100 each)	
	WAXING, FOR YOU	27.00		
	SCOTLAND: 2 x FLIGHTS, HOTELS, CAR HIRE, EXTRAS!	£1430		
	Taxis	£190.00		
	TOTAL	£8203.00		

DATE	ITEM	TOTAL EXPENSES	RECEIPTS	BALANCE
FEBRUARY	Mr Salamone consultation	300-00		
	Lagerfeld dress (½ square metre of material)	3500·00		
	Marks & Spencer - month's supply ready-cooked food	450·00		
	Harrods	72·50		
	Browns (nice of them to accept a cheque)	4854·00		
	French Deli deliveries	262-20		
	Janet Reger	322·60		
	Bubbles: Champagne delivery × 4 crates	5316·00		
	Boots The Chemist	800-00		
	Noskids Dry Cleaners	142·00		
	Tip Hanson, Homeopath (tipped me all night!!)	50·00		
	Southampton Holiday Inn - room, champagne etc, etc...	380·00		
	Mr Magi Yacoub consultation: cellulite removal	400·00		
	Taxis	375·00		
	Restaurants	790·00		
	TOTAL	£18,014·30		

Noskids
Dry Cleaners
ITEM:
Joseph Wool
suit.
Removal of
grass stains on
back of skirt and
jacket
TOTAL £10.39
0116
VAT included

PERSONAL EXPENSES

DATE	ITEM	TOTAL EXPENSES	RECEIPTS	BALANCE
	BOLI JEWELLERS – valued M.'s watch (FAKE!!)	65·00		
	PARIS: flights, hotels, extras(!)	2500·00		
	Restaurant Marie Antoinette – £50 for a ticket & the soup's cold!! F 3612			
	PREMIER COUTURE – F90999	£9·99 – or is that Lira?		
	CHANEL	F14320 – am I losing my touch?		
	INTERFLORA (mummy's flowers)	£100·00		
	LE SKI CLOTHIERS	??– Forgot to keep a record!!		
H	HOSPITAL BILLS	£2500–		
C	French deli delivery – 2 gross french sticks —	150·00		
R	Chauffering services (HUGHIE)	53·00		
A	Bar Mitzvah present (membership to Hurlingham AND £1000 cash)			
M	Dr Jacobson: Injections for Indonesia	£95·00		
	Taxis	109·00		
	Restaurants	£1900·00		
	TOTAL	????.??	!	
	TOTAL			

PERSONAL EXPENSES

DATE	ITEM	TOTAL EXPENSES	RECEIPTS	BALANCE
APRIL	STAG SUITCASES - nice, smooth, buttery, sweaty leather! £300.00			
	INDONESIA: FLIGHT, HOTELS, MASSAGES	£2400.00		
	Rickshaw hire - cheaper to buy one - so, I did!	140.00		
	SILK WARDROBE	100.00		
	Pak Lok Cuk £170.00 per day & well worth it!!			
	Dubai Duty Free	1753.00		
	Vidal Sassoon	98.00		
	Taxis	273.00		
	Donation to Oxfam	£2000.00		
	Restaurants	£2000.00		
	Total: AT LEAST £9744.00			

OXFAM

Thank you
for your generous

Personal Expenses

DATE	ITEM	TOTAL EXPENSES	RECEIPTS	BALANCE
MAY	CLINGFILM - worked well - kept him FRESH!!	50.00		
	Saturn Pharmacy - Vitamins E, C, B, B6, Zinc, Magnesium	£298.00		
	Antigua: Flights, hotel, etc, etc.	£6037.00		
	Harrods - remember to return dress - soiled	£3010.00		
	SELFRIDGES	500.00		
	Tarot reading	£52.00		
	Sotheby's Torture Catalogue - torture to resist anything	£45.00		
	Bar Mitzvah present - membership to Hurlingham AND £1250 cash	£3900.00		
	SHARON - sponsored run to Brixton Prison 10p per mile	60p		
	Taxis	£516.00		
	Restaurants	£1913.00		
	Total (give or take the odd hairdo)			
	TOTAL	£16,321:60		

PERSONAL EXPENSES

DATE	ITEM	TOTAL EXPENSES	RECEIPTS	BALANCE
	Sven's Pressie - leather pouch to put his valuables in.	£63·00		
	Leather cat suit	280·00		
	Rocky & Razor ... or was it Razor then Rocky?	£50·00		
	Post House	£375·00		
JUNE	Champagne Delivery - 1 x crate	579·00		
	Joseph ... Jesus & Mary !! The price!!	£6800·00 !! ↙ maybe I can wear it twice??		
	Dr Levy consultation	524·00		
	Seductive evening for Marcus - what a waste -	£475·00		
		£547·00		
	court tickets to Wimbledon - (Close shave with Agassi)	£160·00		
		£3285·00		
	The Grand Total: £13,138·00			

PERSONAL EXPENSES

DATE	ITEM	TOTAL EXPENSES	RECEIPTS	BALANCE
JULY	New York: flights, hotels, extras	£4530·00		
	BLOOMINGDALES – WONDERFUL SERVICE!!	$20560 – sterling??		
	Boodle & Oodles	7580·00		
	Alistair McCormack security consultation	– £150 –		
	Harrods Facial Testing – mumbled something about walnuts… £100 –			
	Bill Myers – landscape gardening consultation	15·00		
	Window Cleaner. You've heard of window lean…	£60 –		
	knitting machine – more Tracey I think	£199·00		
	Motor mechanics course	£40–00	$20560 ÷ or × ?? = £sterling	
	Photographers fee for retouching photos	£400–00		
	Taxis	£312–00		
	Restaurants	£532–00		
	Total:	£13,918·00 + Bloomingdales		
	How many dollars to the pound?? 6? 7?			
	TOTAL			

DATE	ITEM	TOTAL EXPENSES	RECEIPTS	BALANCE
AUGUST	Wax Factor – ouch!!	23.00		
	Tennis club renewal (open new turf account)	800.00		
	Harrods – new tennis clothes	514.00		
	Larry – Interior Design – 1st payment	540.00		
	'Bubbles' 5 x bottles Pimms no. 5 @ £12.00 each (with Larry's friend, Pym)	60.00		
	SARDINIA: flights, hotels, extras: £4600			
	Taxis	512.00		
	Charity Event with Tracey (for HANDCUFFS, ex-prisoners association)	120–00		
	Tickets to Sunset Boulevard	60.00		
	Restaurants	800.00		
	TOTAL AUGUST TOTAL:	£8,029.00		

Cheap month – is that ALL?

PERSONAL EXPENSES

DATE	ITEM	TOTAL EXPENSES	RECEIPTS	BALANCE
September	BOOK SHOP - bought Freud's Interpretation of Dreams - been having some interesting ones lately... and some other worthy books –	79.00		
	Shaggers Hair Salon	70.00	– The best ~~shag~~ haircut for weeks!!	
	Red Herring Caterers	£600-00		
	Mandy's Wine Bar (RANDY Mandy!!)	245.00		
	Restaurants	£460.00		
	Taxis	£83.00		
	Video Hire	2.50	+	
	+ extra £25.00 to delivery boy for showing me how to work the machine —	25.00		
	Zulu Warriors hire	100-00	each	
	2 months subscription - Weight Watchers –	£100.00	– (Sharon of course).	
	School Uniform	320.00	- GOOD! can still get my size!!	
	TOTAL:	WHO CARES!!		
	TOTAL			

Personal Expenses

DATE	ITEM	TOTAL EXPENSES	RECEIPTS	BALANCE
October	Taxis	370·00		
	Window Cleaner – bought new squeezy...!	93·00		
	THE LOG CHALET & SAUNA COMPANY, consultation	300·00	– some	
	mistake....! I thought THEY were paying		ME??	
	WH Smiths for typewriter ribbon	5·00	– it left	
	a black mark on my forehead....!			
	Flowers for Melanie (what came over me??)	£	50·00	
	French deli delivery – 150 French sticks	40·00		
	Donation to Conservative Party	£2000·00		
	Birthday present for ME! – 1 crate champagne		270·00	
	– 2kgs best Beluga		175·00	
	– 3 of Ann Summer's			
	latest toys.....	£	73·50	
	TOTAL	£3043·50		
	TOTAL			

WARNING
THIS TOY IS NOT SUITABLE FOR ANYONE UNDER THE AGE OF 18

PERSONAL EXPENSES

DATE	ITEM	TOTAL EXPENSES	RECEIPTS	BALANCE
NOVEMBER	Bus Fare	20.00	- no change for note.	
	Wax Factor (no pain, no gain!)	£27.50		
	Lunch with Kelvin	108.00	needed the calories!	
	Dinner with Kelvin	310.00		
	Breakfast with Kelvin	35.00		
	French Deli - emergency supplies	70.00		
	Phone Bill	630.00		
	Video Hire	30.00		
	Restaurants	163.00	- terrible month for entertaining	
	Taxis	£45.00		
	anyone would think I was saving for Christmas! →	TOTAL - £1438.50		
	TOTAL			

DATE	ITEM	TOTAL EXPENSES	RECEIPTS	BALANCE
DECEMBER	O Sole Mio Restaurant, Venice - what a ROMANTIC evening - shame Marcus was ill in bed —	L437000		
	Francesca's - Italian salesmen are SO persuasive —	L9780000		
	Dino's	L64300	??	
	Harrods - Christmas Shopping (always do everything there.) —	£4000·00		
	Fortnum's Christmas & New Year Survival Hamper . . .	£875·00		
	WOOLWORTH'S - last minute shopping for Marcus's relatives —	£63·00		
	Browns a FEW outfits for Christmas -	£5300·00		
	Restaurants	£6070·00		
	Taxis	594·00		
	TOTAL	£16,902 (ex LIRA)		

The Festive Season!!

ANNUAL TOTAL — MUST be less than last year?

DA

The GOLD Card

Please Quote Your Gold Card Number in all Correspondence

1004 753 543 196

Statement of Account

DORIEN GREEN
BRYAN CLOSE
CHIGWELL
ESSEX
CM 12

Statement Date

05/10/94

REF: 21763M

Date Received by us	Reference Number	Description	Previous Balance
			8035.25
		PAYMENT RECEIVED - THANK YOU *well done Marcus*	8000.00
01/09/94	025317	PAMPER DELUXE HEALTH FARM	4534.05
02/09/94	131744	BUSYBEES DRY CLEANING	250.00
04/09/94	146231	PETROL SUNNINGDALE SERVICES	30.00
04/09/9[illegible]	213119	SUNNINGDALE MERCEDES	[illegible]240.00

DATE	ITEM					TOTAL EXPENSES	RECEIPTS	BALANCE

06/09/94	440037	BROWNS, SOUTH MOLTON STREET – A Girl needs cheering up after a car crash	1500.00
10/09/94	541035	HARRODS	2999.99
11/09/94	629399	MARKS AND SPENCER	14.99
15/09/94	461801	F W WOOLWORTHS - Mrs Pearsons birthday - saw a lovely t-shirt in the sale.	3.50
15/09/94	562310	KURT RHEINGOLD ASSOCIATES	1000.00
18/09/94	414923	SELFRIDGES – catering pack of MANHUNTER perfume	1300.00
21/09/94	311214	THE POST HOUSE ← standing Double room reservation	235.00
		New Balance	£ 13142.78

DONT FORGET - YOU WILL GET
20 AIR MILES FOR EVERY £500 SPENT WITH YOUR GOLD CARD

AD97

DETACH HERE AND RETAIN STATEMENT

TOTAL

PERSONAL EXPENSES
BALANCE
RECEIPTS
TOTAL EXPENSES
ACE OF CABS
24 HOUR SERVICE
RADIO CONTROLLED
ESTIMATES ON REQUEST
PHONE
071 777 6666
0779
TREVORS TAXIS
081 787 5060
M.W. OAKS
LICENSED CAB DRIVER
RECEIVED
WITH THANKS
TOTAL
DATE

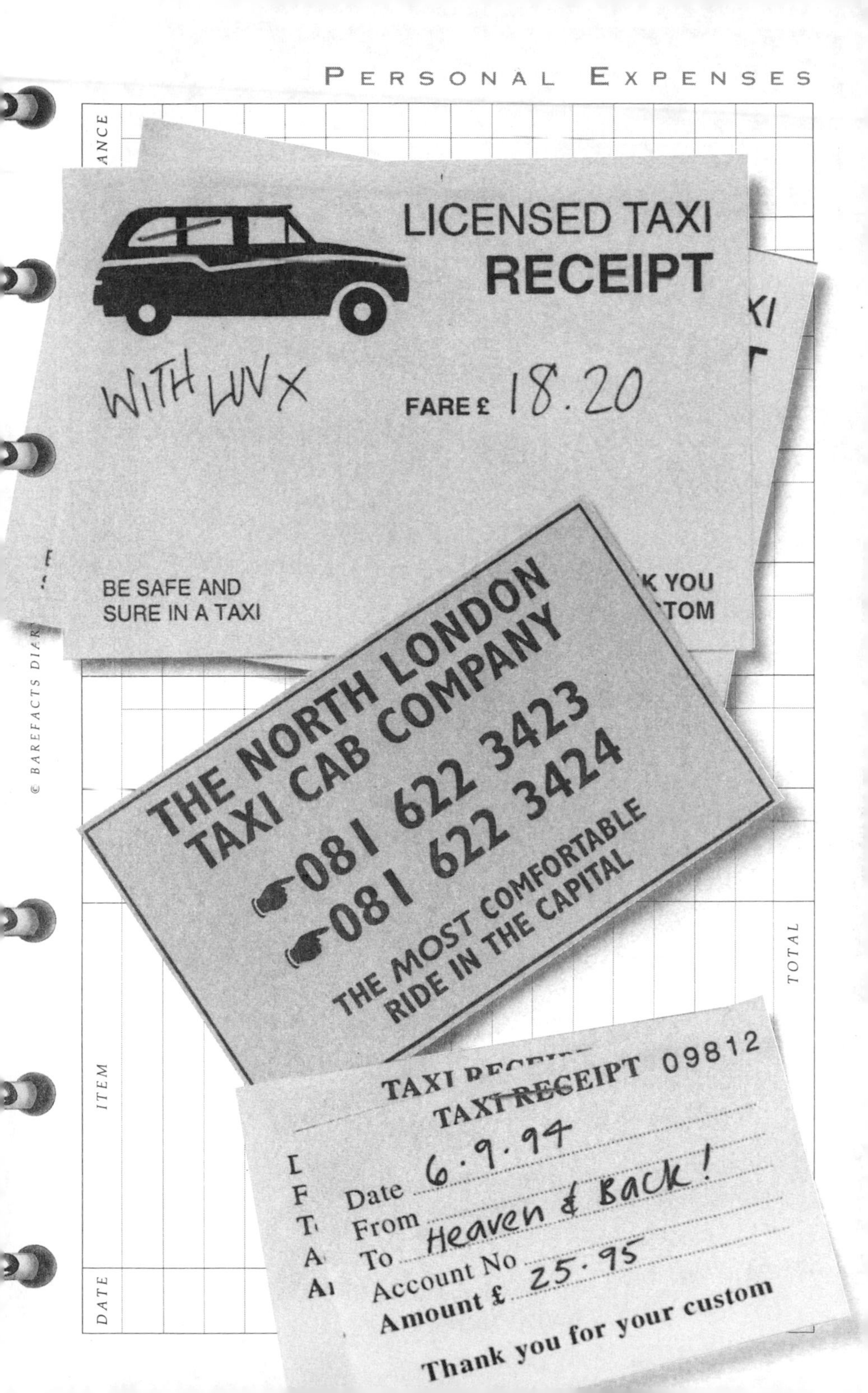
LICENSED TAXI
RECEIPT
WITH LUV X
FARE £ 18.20
BE SAFE AND
SURE IN A TAXI
K YOU
TOM
THE NORTH LONDON
TAXI CAB COMPANY
081 622 3423
081 622 3424
THE MOST COMFORTABLE
RIDE IN THE CAPITAL
TAXI RECEIPT 09812
Date 6.9.94
From
To Heaven & Back!
Account No
Amount £ 25.95
Thank you for your custom
DATE
ITEM
TOTAL

BROGANS

BRASSERIE

13 Gabri

4 x

2 x

2 x

2 x

St. Pierre Restaurant

214 Barkley Mews, London

Telephone 081 456 9123

.00

0.00

£24.00

£120.00

£215.00

La Capallina

RISTORANTE

Thank you for dining at La Capallina. Your meal is itemized as follows:

2 x Prawn Remoulade	£18.50
2 x Marinated Trout Florentine	£65.00
2 x La Capallina Love Truffles	£30.00
2 x Bottle of Chablis	£70.00
Total	£183.50

We hope you enjoyed your time with us and we look forward to repeating this pleasure

17 St. Matthews Gardens, London.

Telephone 071 009 9963

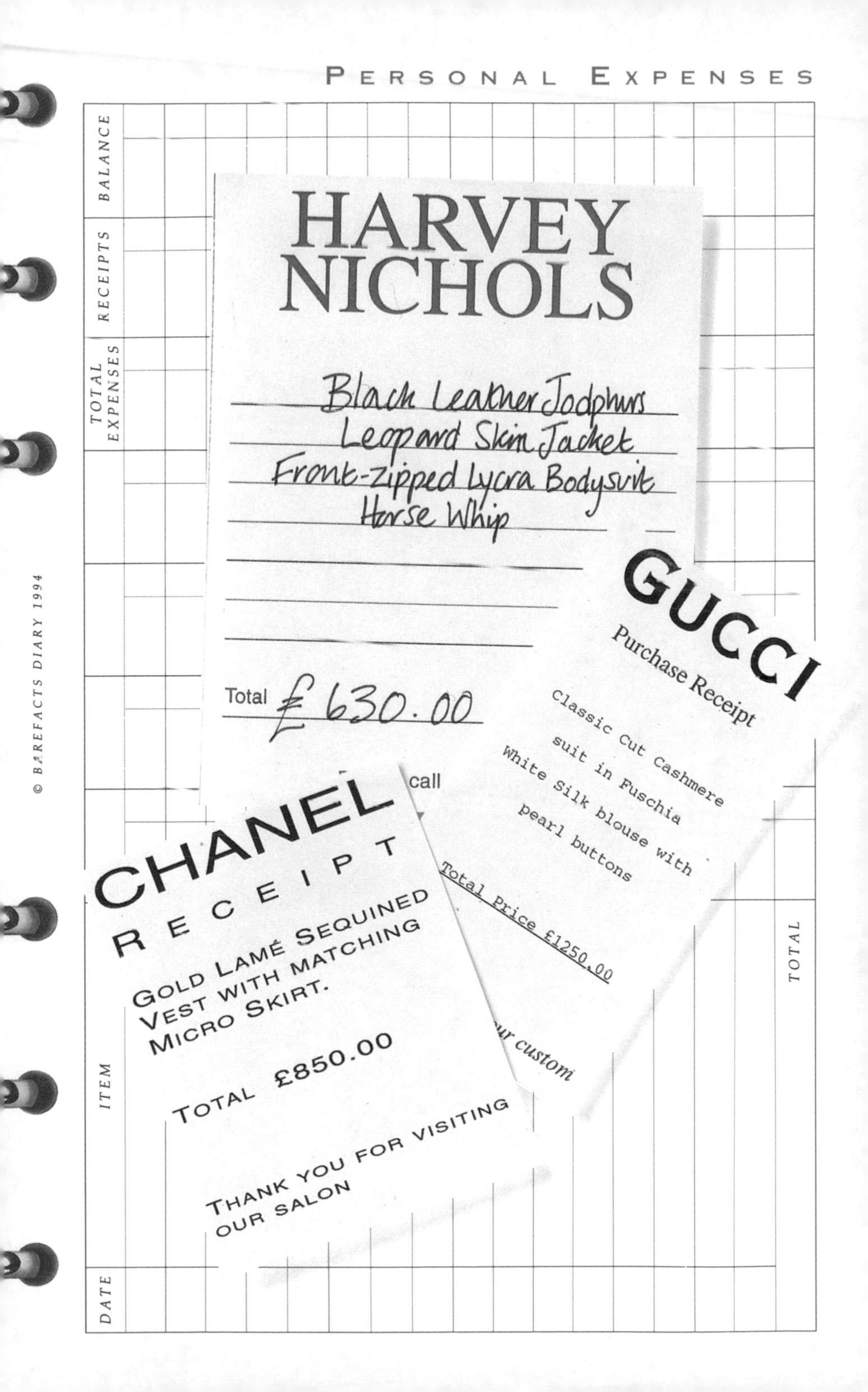
PERSONAL EXPENSES
BALANCE
RECEIPTS
TOTAL EXPENSES
ITEM
DATE
TOTAL
© BAREFACTS DIARY 1994
HARVEY NICHOLS
Black Leather Jodphurs
Leopard Skin Jacket
Front-zipped Lycra Bodysuit
Horse Whip
Total £630.00
GUCCI
Purchase Receipt
Classic Cut Cashmere
suit in Fuschia
White Silk blouse with
pearl buttons
Total Price £1250.00
CHANEL
RECEIPT
GOLD LAMÉ SEQUINED
VEST WITH MATCHING
MICRO SKIRT.
TOTAL £850.00
THANK YOU FOR VISITING
OUR SALON

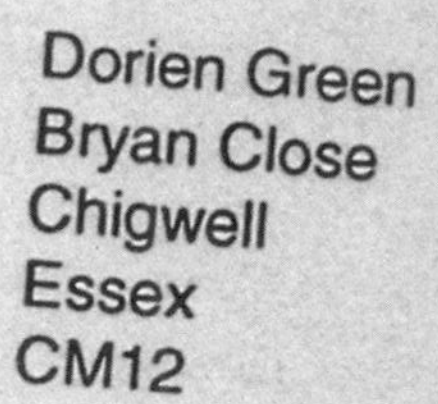

THE HONEY TREE HEALTH FARM

HONEY TREE LANE
MORETON-IN-THE-MARSH
GLOUCESTERSHIRE
GL19 4HF
TELEPHONE: 0981 359
FAX: 0981 658

Dorien Green
Bryan Close
Chigwell
Essex
CM12

INVOICE NO. 52130

2 Nights de luxe suite @ £250
(Including Half Board)

Aroma rapy £5

... s @ £25
(all with Kurt by request)

Private hire of jacuzzi for 1 night	£200
Extras: Baby Oil - 10 litres @ £3.50	£300
Condoms - 2 dozen @ 50p	£35
	£12
Phonecalls from husband dealt with 3 @ £50	£150
SUB-TOTAL	£1247.00
VAT @ 17.5%	£187.05
TOTAL	£1434.05

Thank you for calling and please come again soon

PERSONAL EXPENSES

NOTES

NOTES

DATE	NAME	AGE	CARD	GIFT
26.2	Melanie Fishman – (must remember to forget it)			
5.3	MUMMY	73	✓	✓
	(standing order of white lilies in sympathy)			
31.3	Marcus's Auntie Sadie			✓
	REMEMBER – she's on her last legs!			
14.5	Marcus's Uncle Harry – DITTO			
15.6	MARCUS	?	✓	✓
26.6	FATHER			
30.9	Sharon	not as old as she looks!		✓
	Star Sign — LIBRA			
27.10	*My birthday* — SCORPIO			
19.12	Tracey	?	✓	✓
	Star Sign: SAGITTARIUS			I suppose so!

BOOKS I'VE READ THIS YEAR

* The Importance of Being Earnest- Oscar Wilde (only read ½)

* In Praise of Panty Hose - Sabina Sedgewick (wow!)

* My Secret Garden - Nancy Friday (must try some out!)

* Herbs for Youthful Skin-Crescent Smith

* Facial Workout -Colin Sears

* The Cellulite War – Dr. James Honey

* Healthy, Wealthy & Wise - A Guide to Success - Myra Browning, MBA, PhD, ETA

* The Joy of Eternal Youth... and how to achieve it - Alaison Mary Reynolda.

* CARS THAT ARE GOOD TO DO IT IN:

1. Rolls ✓
2. Jag ✓
3. BIG Mercedes ✓

* CARS THAT ARE BAD TO DO IT IN:

1. All reps cars with hangers on the grab handle. X
2. Marcus's car (how to explain away heel marks on roof lining?) X
3. Cars with alarms that go off if they rock too hard!! X

You are invited to the
exclusive preview
of
THE NEW COLLECTION
OF BARELY THERE SWIMWEAR
4th May - 7.30 pm
277 South Melton Street, London.
Wine & a light buffet will be served

B·I·T·E

They're stunning -
Almost indecent!

Are you SINGLE
and living in
NORTH LONDON?
Are you aged 30-45?
Do you enjoy good food and
good company?
Call us now
081 632 5555
must
investigate !!
SLIM
for
SUMMER
£10 OFF
YOUR FIRST VISIT
WITH THIS VOUCHER
• Medically supervised weight loss
• Weekly consultation with our doctor
• £15 a visit, including all medication
• Range of diets and treatments available
to suit your lifestyle.
• Massage by vibration.
The Chigwell Slimming Centre.
2nd floor, 216 High Street, Chigwell. ☎ 081 622 2323

Dear Dorien,

Saw your car - haven't seen you for a while - sure you've been busy - we ought to get together again sometime....

Chelmsford Football Team

I'm getting on a bit but I'll do my best!

Jodie x

Milk is good for you

NDUSTRIAL

ON DAIRIES

Milkman

2 pints of cream please

x

To my Valentine

xxx

~~only~~ only six roses - still, it's the thought that counts.

Was this from Simon??

With Love to my Valentine

EXCLUSIVE LINGERIE BY POST

Mare Sainer
AGONY AUNT

Monday 9th May 1994

Dear Doris of Chigwell,

I found your letter fascinating, but far too outré to print in the delicate columns of the Sunday Sport. Your sort of condition is not rare, but be re-assured, you are not a nymphomaniac. Nymphomania is a morbid condition and sufferers do not actually enjoy sex. Not your problem I fear.

It seems to me your main hang-up is simply classic Jewish guilt vis à vis hubbie and mum. And why not? you're a size ten, rich,gorgeous, and you get laid 15 times a week. You want to feel good too? Okay, I admit it, I'm jealous.

Keep taking the precautions.

Mare.

Thank GOD for that!!
I'm normal!
(shame she couldn't publish)

Notes

Found this fascinating old print in 'Astro Monthly'!

Gemini

no wonder M. has big... shoulders.

Scorpio- what an INTERESTING part of the body to be associated to!!

Melanie 'fishfeet' Fishman.

SCORPIO SCORPIO

STAR OF THE MONTH

Scorpio (Oct 23 - Nov 22)

Your stormy passionate side will come to the fore this year as you discover the true depths of your sensuality. Many people will find your mysterious Scorpio nature hypnotically fascinating. Enjoy life to the full as Scorpios need feel no guilt.

My BEST ever horoscope

Can't decide between Jasper's healing hands or Dr Fortuna's crystal balls !!?

PSYCHIC COUNSELLING

Relax in the warm healing hands of Jasper highly experienced medium who will devote himself to your spiritual developement

CALL 081 463 6655
Day or night

- DISCOVER your own psychic powers - learn how to make others reveal all. 071 010 3321
- TRANSFORMATION, EMPOWERMENT Astrological reading. 081 456 9933
- QUALIFIED EXPERIENCED and truly caring psychic readings - A thrilling experience. 071 008 6692

DR FORTUNA

AVAILABLE DAY (OR NIGHT)
TAROT CARDS
CRYSTAL BALLS
ASTROLOGY
NO APPOINTMENT NECESSARY
(WE'LL BE EXPECTING YOU)
CALL 081 001 0101

ALSO A LARGE SELECTION OF BOOKS, EQUIPMENT AND PARAPHERNALIA

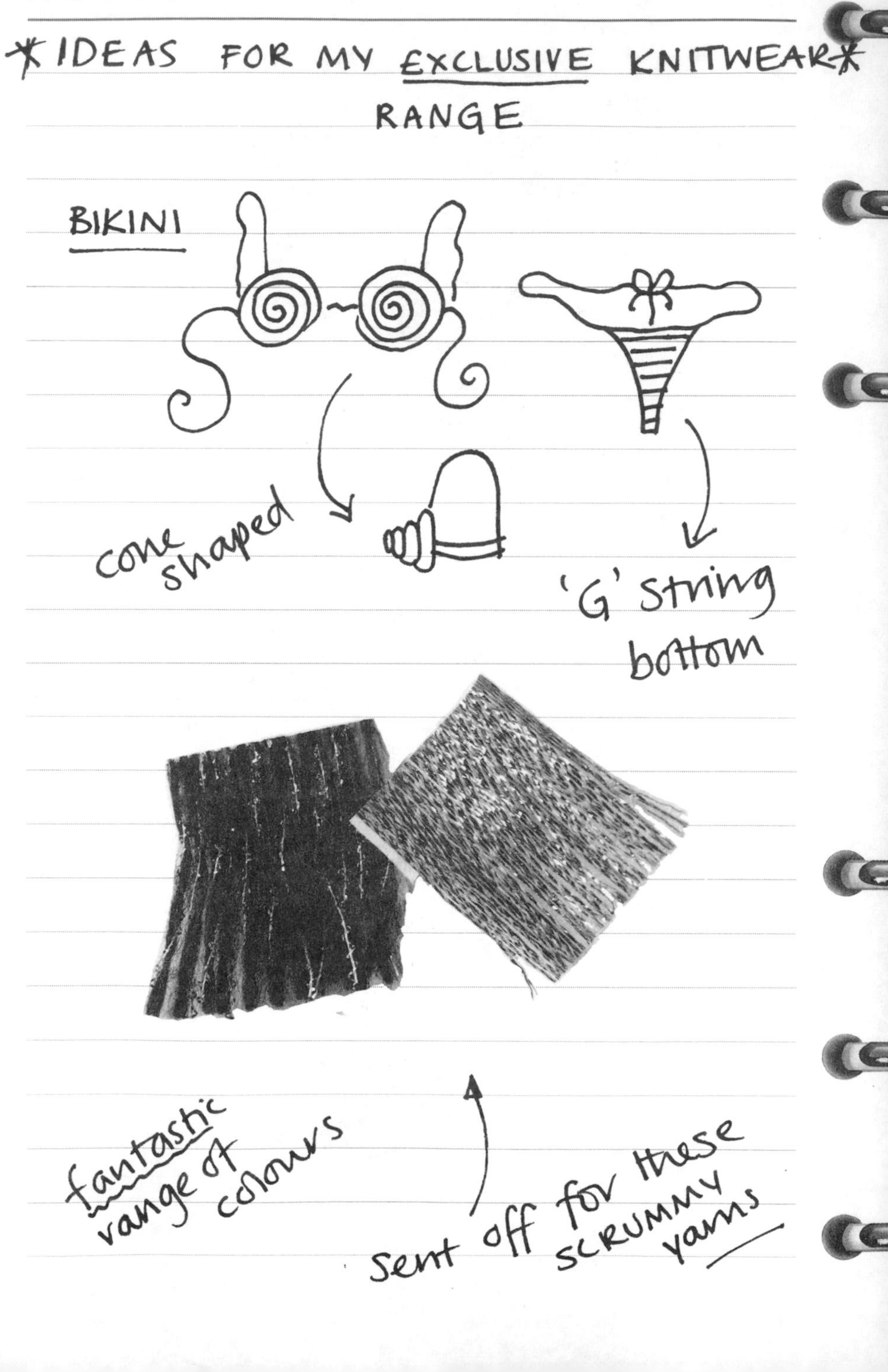
IDEAS FOR MY EXCLUSIVE KNITWEAR
RANGE
BIKINI
cone shaped
'G' string bottom
fantastic range of colours
sent off for these SCRUMMY yarns

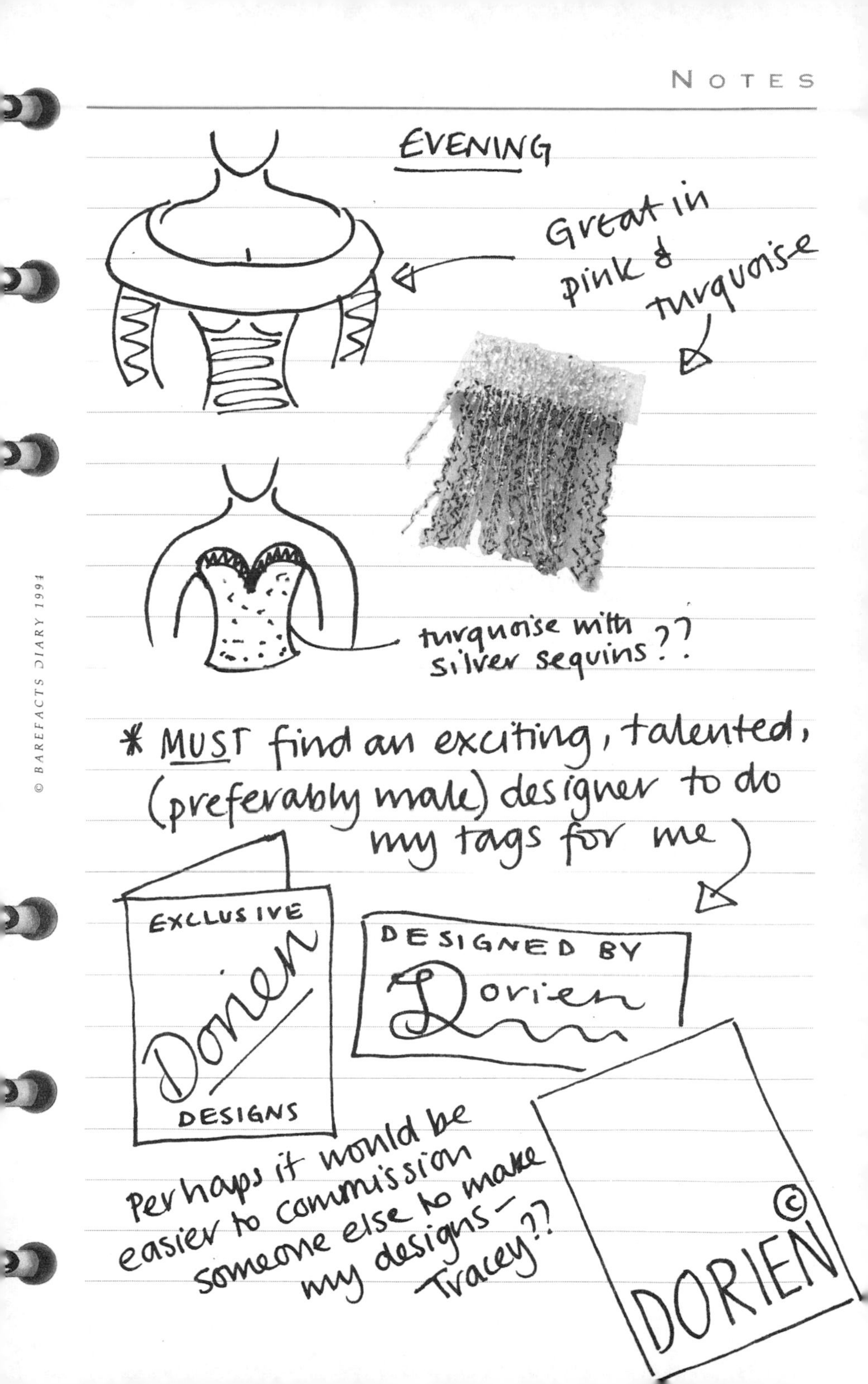
NOTES
EVENING
Great in pink & turquoise
turquoise with silver sequins??
* MUST find an exciting, talented, (preferably male) designer to do my tags for me)
EXCLUSIVE
Dorien
DESIGNS
DESIGNED BY
Dorien
Perhaps it would be easier to commission someone else to make my designs – Tracey??
©
DORIEN
© BAREFACTS DIARY 1994

26 UPPER GROUND
LONDON SE1 9PD
TELEPHONE 071-620 1666
FACSIMILE 071-620 1314

1st July 199

Dorien Green
Bryan Close
Chigwell
Essex CM12

A delight indeed!

What a delight it was visiting you last week to discuss publishing possibilities for your manuscript indulgence. I confess had I known the meeting was to be so informal I would have brought a coat-hanger. It was very kind of you to show me over the house and garden and let me see your holiday snaps. Please accept my sympathies about your husband Marcus. His breakdown must have been a great trial to you.

To your book. I have now had time to read the manuscript thoroughly and although it has great potential I'm afraid the prevailing economic climate makes new novelists difficult to establish. I am very much afraid therefore, I am unable offer you any publishing proposals at the present time. Please do keep in touch.

All best wishes.

Yours sincerely

Trevor Dolby
EDITORIAL DIRECTOR

July 8th 1997

Dear Mrs Green

Your visit to Pavilion's offices was rather startling. The pictures were, as was obvious, a bit of a shock. Believe me it had not occurred to me for one moment that I was ruining your life and that I had taken advantage of you. I would also suggest that any newspaper editor worth his salt would notice immediately that my head had been pasted onto the naked body of William Baldwin and your face onto Sharon Stone's. Please be aware that I am not susceptible to blackmail.

Yours sincerely

Trevor Dolby
EDITORIAL DIRECTOR

PAVILION
26 UPPER GROUND
LONDON SE1 9PD
TELEPHONE 071-620 1666
FACSIMILE 071-620 1314

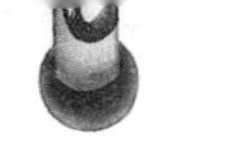

Dorien Green
Bryan Close
Chigwell
Essex CM12

15th July 1994

Yippee!! Good old Kelvin!

Dear Mrs Green

I confess the letter from Kelvin McKenzie was unexpected. Under the circumstances I would be delighted to publish you novel.

Yours sincerely

Trevor Dolby
EDITORIAL DIRECTOR

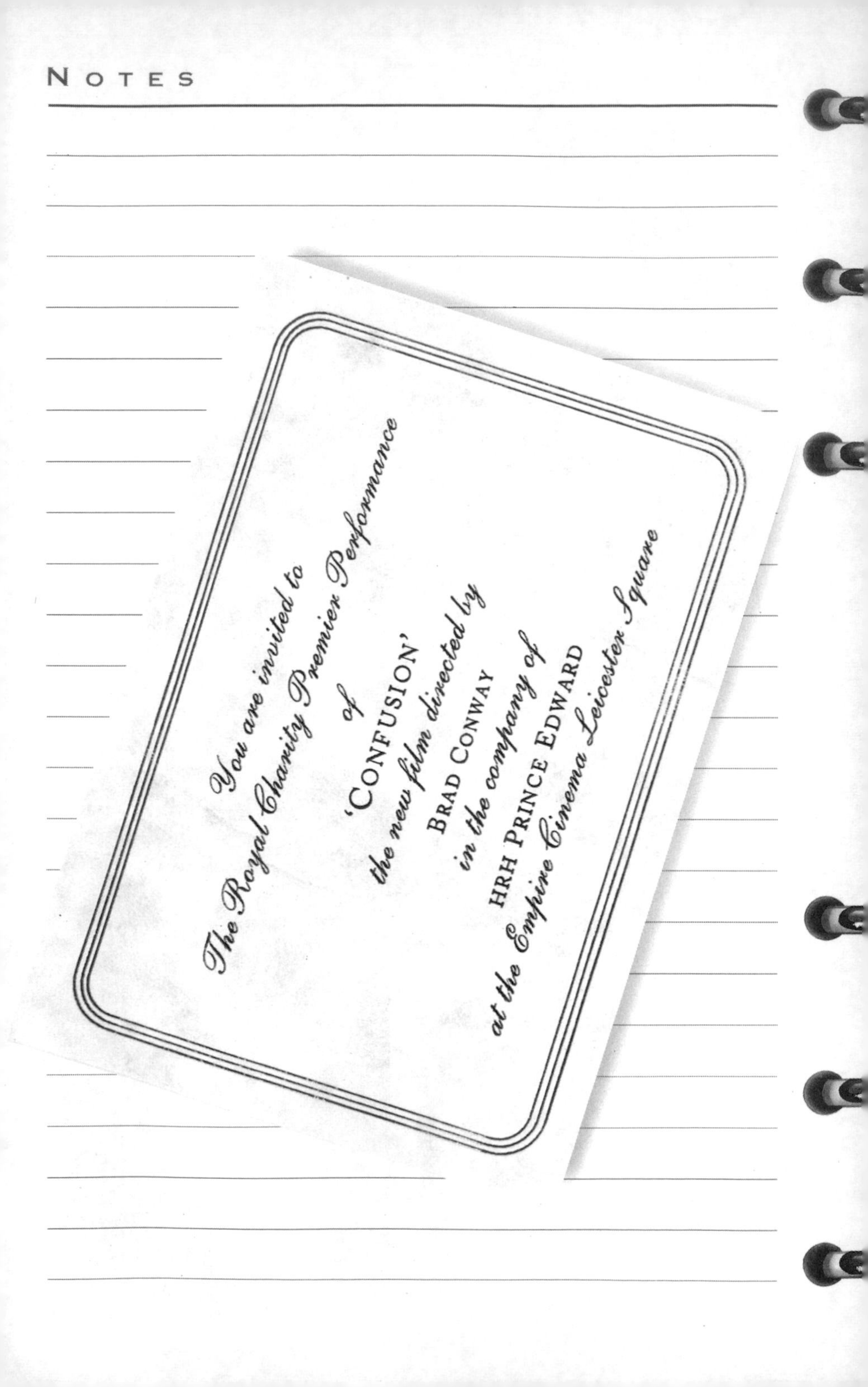
NOTES
You are invited to
The Royal Charity Premier Performance
of
'CONFUSION'
the new film directed by
BRAD CONWAY
in the company of
HRH PRINCE EDWARD
at the Empire Cinema Leicester Square

moneylink

ACC NO: 212167348

VALID FROM: 8/93 EXPIRES END: 8/95

MRS D. GREEN

THE TOYBOY CLUB

MEMBERSHIP No: 6 7 2 4 9 3 7 1

NAME: Miss D. Green

SIGNATURE: Miss D.Green

OPENING HOURS
10pm - [illegible]am Weekdays
[illegible]pm - [illegible]am Fri & Sat • Closed Sundays

BB MEMBERSHIP CARD

MEMBERSHIP NO: 16A HOZ61/ZPR

LEVEL OF SERVICE: RESCUE AND RECOVERY

VALID UNTIL: 06/05/95

THE BREAKDOWN BOYS

WORLD BANK

£100

ACC. NO. 627153916

VALID FROM 05/93 MRS D GREEN

EXPIRES END 08/95 61-92-77 0078554308

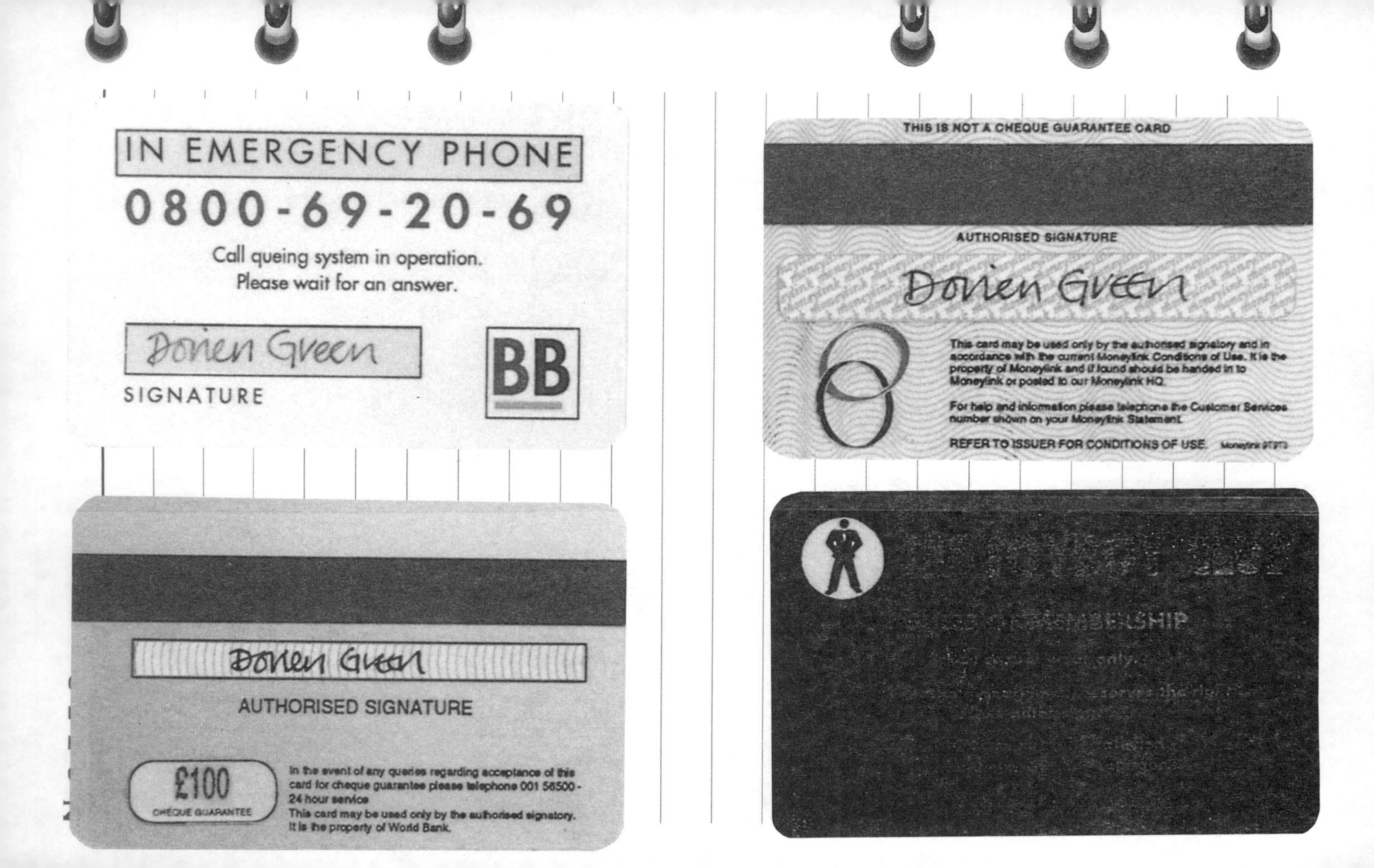
IN EMERGENCY PHONE
0800-69-20-69
Call queing system in operation.
Please wait for an answer.
Dorien Green
SIGNATURE
BB
THIS IS NOT A CHEQUE GUARANTEE CARD
AUTHORISED SIGNATURE
Dorien Green
This card may be used only by the authorised signatory and in accordance with the current Moneylink Conditions of Use. It is the property of Moneylink and if found should be handed in to Moneylink or posted to our Moneylink HQ.
For help and information please telephone the Customer Services number shown on your Moneylink Statement.
REFER TO ISSUER FOR CONDITIONS OF USE.
Dorien Green
AUTHORISED SIGNATURE
£100
CHEQUE GUARANTEE
In the event of any queries regarding acceptance of this card for cheque guarantee please telephone 001 56500 - 24 hour service
This card may be used only by the authorised signatory.
It is the property of World Bank.

ACKNOWLEDGEMENTS

The publishers would like to thank:

Carole Bennett, Dash (tennis gear), Troy Halliday, Helen Holmes, Suzie Hooper, Kerry Ann Hurst, Herbert Johnson (Dorien's hat and hat boxes), Stephen Keane, Lillywhites (tennis gear), Francis Loney, Sandy McCullough, Claire McGee, Kelley-Anne McGee, Helen Mitchell, Vivien Placks, Scott Robinson, Keith Saunders, Linda Siefert, Jeremy Thomas.

NOTES

THE END

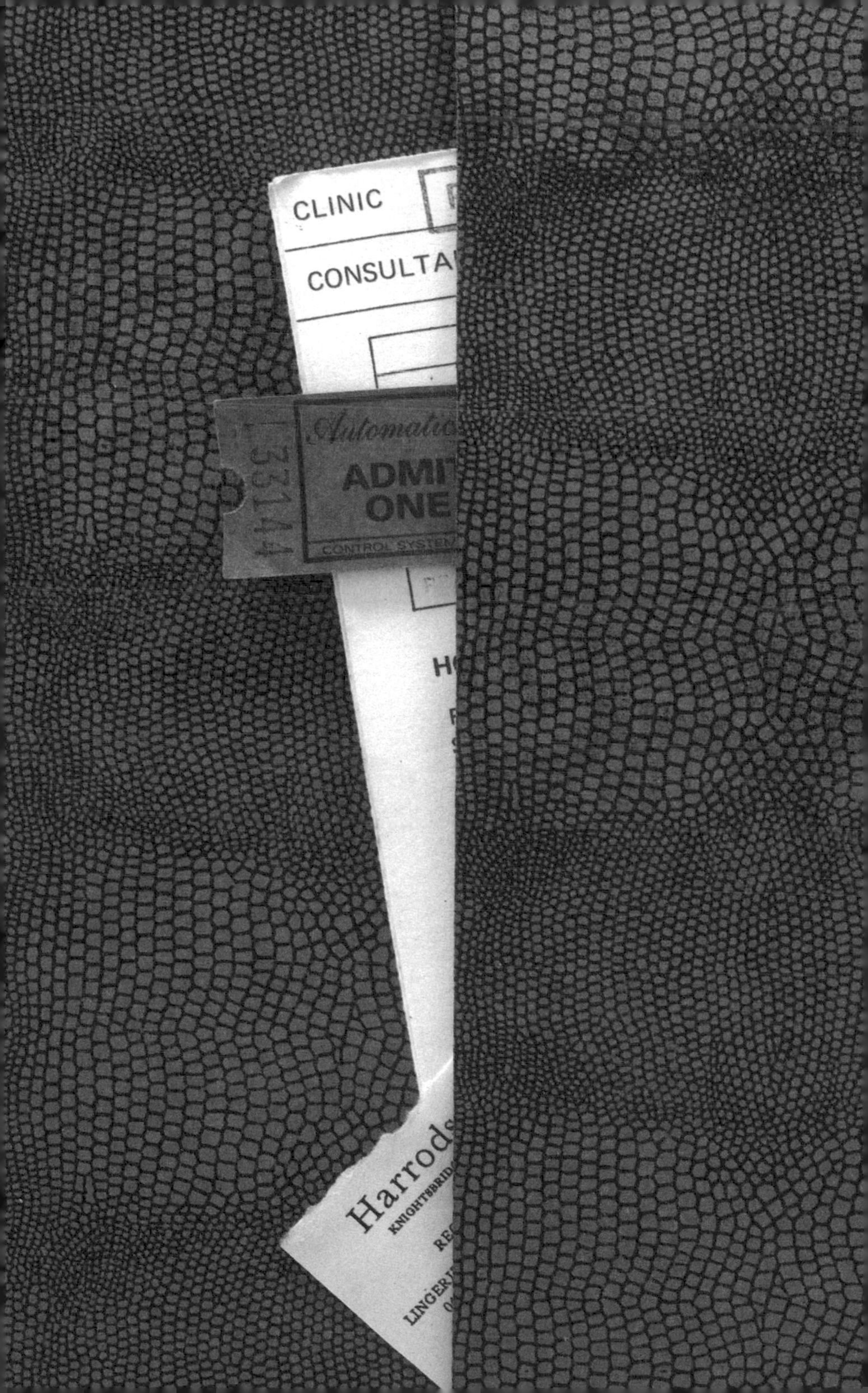
CLINIC
ONE
Harrods